TERRAPIN'S POT OF SENSE

Other books by the same author:

THE COW-TAIL SWITCH and other West African stories
(*with George Herzog*)

THE FIRE ON THE MOUNTAIN and other Ethiopian stories
(*with Wolf Leslau*)

THE HOT SHAKING DANCE and other tales from the Gold Coast

KANCHIL'S LIME PIT and other stories from Indonesia

HAITI SINGING

THE CABALLERO

TERRAPIN'S
POT OF SENSE

by Harold Courlander

ILLUSTRATED BY ELTON FAX

HOLT, RINEHART AND WINSTON
New York · Chicago · San Francisco

Library of Congress Catalog Card Number: 57-11682

Published, November, 1957
Second Printing, October, 1958
Third Printing, October, 1961
Fourth Printing, October, 1964
Fifth Printing, September, 1966

91581-0614

Printed in the United States of America

DEDICATED TO RICH AMERSON,
MINSTREL AND STORY TELLER
OF SUMTER COUNTY, ALABAMA,
SARAH AMERSON, AND
EARTHY ANNE COLEMAN

CONTENTS

TERRAPIN'S POT OF SENSE

WAITING ON SALVATION

Now just set there, boy, and listen what I'm tellin' you. You too, girl, quiet down and quit scratchin' yourself. That's to say, *if* you want to hear what I got to tell you about Buh Terrapin, Buh Fox, and the likes of them, includin' Buh 'Gator, of course, not to mention Buh Buzzard and Buh Raven; and I'm not for-gettin' Buh Hawk and Buh Bullfrog *and* Buh Deer. And just because I didn't call on him by name don't mean I ain't got Buh Rabbit in mind, him the smartest of the lot.

So just sit back and listen, and don't ask me no more questions.

The kind of world we livin' in, critters and humanfolks spend a powerful lot of time tryin' to outsmart each other, tryin' to test which is the best man amongst 'em. You got big animals like Buh Elephant, and stout ones like Buh Bull, and in a test of *strength* they pretty sure to come out on top.

But they's another thing in this world—intellect. When God gave out different things to different critters he gave 'em all some-thing special to make up for what they didn't get. Take Buh Fox, now. He's no good in a fight with Buh Wolf; Buh Wolf can just about swallow him whole, isn't that the truth? But Buh Fox got special knowledge how to get his dinner on the sly and get back to his den. Buh Weasel, now, he ain't big or strong, but he's faster'n forked lightnin'.

You see, we got what you call *elements* in this world, too. They always fightin' each other. We got water, and we got sunshine. Sometimes the sun burnin' everything up, then we get rain to cool everything off. You think rain's the most powerful? Well, the first thing you know the sun shine on the water and dry it all up again. So who's the stoutest, sun or water? It's the same thing with the animals. Sometimes size gives strength. Buh Bull, now, he ain't afraid of dogs or goats or nothin'. But Buh Mosquito can sure give him a bad time, now, can't he? So size ain't everything.

But they's other elements, like *direction*. Take Buh Bat. Never saw no hawk could catch a bat on the wing. Buh Bat is sure fast, but he fly the zigzaggedest course you ever see, enough to drive you crazy. Take Buh Horse. He's good on the straightaway; but when he get to a big, high fence he's got to call a halt. Buh Rabbit, on the other hand, when he get to a fence he goes right through a hole no bigger'n your hand.

It's the same with humanfolks. Some of 'em are big, some small. Some are strong, some weak. Some are dull, and some are sharp. And it ain't easy to figure out in a situation just which one of these here elements goin' to win out. But one thing is sure. Intellect ain't nothin' to sneeze at.

Let me give you a notion of what I mean. It's about Buh Hawk and Buh Buzzard. The way it was, old Buh Hawk came a-flyin' over a cornfield, and when he look down he see Buh Buzzard settin' on the ground there lookin' miserable, his head droopin', just starvin' to death.

Buh Hawk call out, "Kaaa, kaaa, what you doin' down there, Buh Buzzard?"

Buh Buzzard say, "Just starvin' to death, Buh Hawk, just starvin' to death."

"Well," Buh Hawk say, "what you waitin' on anyway?"

And Buh Buzzard say, "I'm waitin' on the salvation of the Lord to feed me, that's what I'm waitin' on."

Buh Hawk laughed at that. He say, "When you goin' to get some sense in your head, Buh Buzzard? You shouldn't never wait on the salvation of the Lord to feed you. You got to go and get it yourself. If you just keep on settin' there waitin' for salvation, you goin' to starve to death 'fore tomorrow night."

"What you think I should do?" Buh Buzzard say.

Buh Hawk went, "Kaaa!" He say, "You hear me hollerin'? I'm huntin' for my dinner. Just watch me. I'm goin' to have somethin' to eat in the next thirty minutes. Goin' to chase Buh Rabbit onto new ground, where he got no place to hole up, and I can dive down and get him. How you like to eat rabbit with me?"

Buh Buzzard shake his head. "Thank you, Buh Hawk, but you know I can't eat fresh meat. I got to let it set for a day or two to smell up and get seasoned."

Buh Hawk say, "Well, I sure feel sorry for you, Buh Buzzard. There's Buh Rabbit now. Watch me go down on him and get him."

Just then Buh Hawk saw Buh Rabbit tearin' 'cross the new ground, and he folded his wings and dove down on him.

"Here I go, Buh Buzzard, watch me!"

Well, listen, Buh Hawk came a-sailin' out of the sky on Buh Rabbit, and he was just about to get him when Buh Rabbit ducked into a hollow stump. Buh Hawk couldn't stop, he flew against that stump and broke his neck.

Buh Buzzard been watchin' everything. Buh Rabbit, inside the hollow stump, he call out to Buh Buzzard: "Come and get him, Buh Buzzard! Me and God will feed you!"

And Buh Buzzard say, "Thank you, Lord, for answerin' my prayer. I'll just let Buh Hawk lay there a day or two to smell up and get seasoned, then I'll eat him."

Now then, you see Buh Hawk thought Buh Buzzard was a fool, but the way it turned out, Buh Buzzard outsmarted Buh Hawk.

REFORM MEETING

O NE THING IS CERTAIN. We got to take into consideration that everyone got his good points as well as bad. And if we don't, we ain't foolin' no one but ourselves. If we think we got all the good points on our side, and the other folks got none, sooner or later we goin' to have to eat crow, and that taste pretty miserable. You always got to give other folks credit for havin' somethin' on their side of the argument.

One time there was a big gatherin' of animals and fowls and birds to talk about everybody behavin' better. Instead of talkin' about doin' better, they start to tell what other folks doin' bad. Buh Hyena up and complained about the way Buh Buzzard was carryin' on. Seems his complaint was Buzzard was gettin' there first to eat. Then Buh Wildcat complained about the troublesome mice and rats. 'Pears like he liked to eat mice and rats real good. Then Buh Tiger up and groaned about the rabbits, sayin' they was the worst of all.

Old Buh Coon he couldn't stand the way the talk was goin', and he called the meetin' to order. "Friends," Buh Coon say, "we all got to do a lot better or we're goin' to end up in bad shape. What have you all got to say about reformin' ourselves?"

Buh Tiger he talk right up. "I'm for reform," he say. "I see Buh Coon stealin' corn every night, and it got to stop."

Then Sister Cow come in with, "I'm for reform too. Buh Tiger he got the blood of my young ones in his mouth, and it got to stop."

Buh Elephant say his piece then: "Look who talkin' about things which got to stop. Sister Cow is eatin' up all the grass, and leave nothin' for the Elephant."

Buh Wolf chime in with his song, sayin', "Men are goin' around carryin' guns and knives, and it isn't safe no more to go after 'em."

Buh Coon he call the meetin' to order again. "We got to have less complaints and more reform," he say. "Who is got somethin' to suggest?"

Well, Buh Deer pop right up and say all the animals got to stop eatin' meat. Buh Wolf don't like that proposition, and he say what's needed is for all the animals to stop eatin' grass. Sister Chicken she say they all miss the main point, which is that they got to kill all the snakes. Then Buh Fox say, "No, I rent my cave to the snakes. What we got to do is kill all the worms." The birds don't like that at all, figurin' to starve if the worms are killed. So they all kept at it, everybody tryin' to keep what was good for himself and get rid of what his neighbor wanted.

At last old Buh Coon rise up and say: "Now if any of you folks are agreeable to get rid of something you like for *yourself*, say so." But didn't nobody say a word, just set so quiet you could hear the potato vines growin'.

"This is sure a sinful world we are livin' in," Buh Coon say, "but when everybody just find fault with everybody else, it's time to quit and go back where you come from. You got to begin charity next door. But if you want to *reform*, it's got to begin at home."

RABBIT, FOX, AND THE RAIL FENCE

Now, BUH FOX is always catchin' hold of Buh Rabbit, 'count of Rabbit always seekin' ways to mischief Buh Fox. The things Buh Rabbit done to Buh Fox is just about too many to count on a caterpillar's toes. And Buh Fox he always studyin' about how he goin' to do away with Rabbit. Well, one time Buh Fox had Buh Rabbit all tied up with a rope, leadin' him 'cross the field. Rabbit was walkin' along just like he goin' to a picnic, pretend he just enjoyin' the walk mighty fine.

He say, "Buh Fox, where we goin' to this mornin'?"

Buh Fox he say, "Buh Rabbit, you done give me a mess of trouble, and I goin' to fix you up good this time. But I just think I'll take you to Tuscaloosa first and show the pretty girls what I caught. How you like that?"

'Bout this time Buh Rabbit's mind begin to work. When they come to a rail fence, he say: "Why, Buh Fox, seems to me we can go right through the rails here and save ourselves a parcel of walkin'."

"You think so?" Buh Fox say.

"I'll show you," Buh Rabbit say. "Just slack up on that rope a minute."

Buh Fox slack up on the rope and Buh Rabbit go right through the fence. Rabbit mighty good at runnin' through a fence, you know. But Buh Fox he say, "Well, I don't know if I can get through that hole, it look small to me."

Rabbit he say, "Slack up a little more, Buh Fox, and I'll raise up on this rail to allow you through."

Fox he slack up a bit, and Buh Rabbit raise up on the rail. He make just about room for Buh Fox's head.

Buh Fox ain't sure about it, but Buh Rabbit say: "Well, doggone, look at them pretty girls from Tuscaloosa!"

Fox say "Where?" and he stick his head through the hole right between the rails.

Right then Rabbit lets down on the rail and say, "You see the pretty girls from Tuscaloosa?"

Fox say, "Ouch. You chokin' me, Buh Rabbit!"

"I ain't asked you that, Buh Fox. I asked you do you see the pretty girls from Tuscaloosa?"

Buh Fox squirmin' and wrigglin' in the fence, and say, "Ouch, Buh Rabbit, I believe you breakin' my neck!"

Buh Rabbit bear down on the rail a little and say, "That ain't what I'm talkin' about, Buh Fox. I asked you do you see the girls?"

Buh Fox say, "Ouch, I'm givin' out!"

Rabbit say, "Let go the rope, Buh Fox."

Buh Fox didn't know what he doin' 'bout this time so he just let go the rope. And Rabbit he just walked off, leavin' Fox caught in the rail fence, his tongue hangin' out, gaggin' and hollerin', just about choked to death. Ain't that Rabbit a smart one?

BUH RABBIT'S TIGHT NECKTIE

YOU LIKE TO HEAR about Buh Rabbit and Blacksnake? Well, perk your ears up then, 'cause that's what I'm talkin' about. You know, Mr. Blacksnake lives in the stone pile at night, and he comes out in the daytime to hunt for mice and things. Now it gets pretty cold in them stone piles in the nighttime, especially around January. And when Mr. Blacksnake gets cold, he gets so sluggish he don't hardly move at all. One mornin' Mr. Blacksnake come out of his rock pile just about froze to death. He was so cold he just about made it, and he crawled into a patch of sun to warm up and thaw out. He was just layin' there, not botherin' anybody.

Just about this time Buh Rabbit come along, hoppin' and skippin' 'cross the new ground on his way to visit the girls at the other side of the field. When he see Buh Blacksnake layin' there nice and quiet, Buh Rabbit say: "Well, look at that, will you? I reckon I can use that to make me a real pretty necktie."

You know what Buh Rabbit do then? He pick up Mr. Blacksnake and hang him around his neck . . . twist him around this way and that way and tie him up in the front into a real fancy bow. Buh Rabbit real proud of himself, figurin' to cut a sharp picture

21

with the girls, all dressed up with a black necktie. In no time at all Buh Rabbit was settin' with the girls in front of the fireplace, carryin' on and laughin' "Ha-ha-ha," like that, havin' a fine time.

But by settin' in front of the fire, the heat began to thaw Mr. Blacksnake up. Buh Blacksnake commence to pullin' down on Buh Rabbit, tightenin' up a bit around his neck. When Rabbit feel the squeeze, he holler: "Pass my hat quick, I'm on business, I got to go!" Rabbit was scared that Blacksnake goin' to swallow him. "Hurry up, girls," he holler, "I'm on business!" Buh Rabbit lit out of the house and say, "Hey, Buh Blacksnake, you chokin' me."

Blacksnake he reply, "Buh Rabbit, you know you treat me wrong. You picked me up when I was so cold I couldn't move, and carried me 'mongst all them girls like I was a common old necktie. Now I'm mad, and I'm goin' to eat you up."

"Wait a minute," Rabbit say, "don't start just yet. Maybe I didn't treat you right before, but I can treat you right now."

"How you goin' to do that?" Mr. Blacksnake ask him.

"Let me take you back where I brought you from. That way you won't have to crawl with a big meal like me in you," Buh Rabbit say. "How you like that?"

"All right," Blacksnake say, "carry me home."

Rabbit tote Blacksnake right back to where he found him in the first place. Then he said, "All right, Buh Blacksnake, slack off now and get ready to eat."

Mr. Blacksnake slacked off Rabbit's neck onto the ground.

"All right now," Rabbit say, "how you want to lay?"

"This'll do fine," Blacksnake say. His mouth begin to water already, thinkin' 'bout eatin' Buh Rabbit.

"Tell you what," Buh Rabbit say, "you just back down in that hole you come out of, with your head stickin' out. If you eat me first, you goin' to be so full you can't get in."

"That's a fine idea, Buh Rabbit," Blacksnake say. He backed down into the hole in the rock pile till only his head was stickin' out.

"You ready now, Buh Blacksnake?" Rabbit ask him.

"Yeah, I'm ready," Blacksnake say.

"You *all* ready?" Buh Rabbit say.

"Yeah, didn't I say I'm ready?" Buh Blacksnake say. "Come on, I'm hungry!"

"Well then, just look over yonder a bit and open your mouth," Rabbit say.

Buh Blacksnake looked away a little and opened his mouth. Rabbit grabbed some sand and threw it in Blacksnake's eyes. Blacksnake couldn't see a thing. Rabbit hopped off that rock pile and headed for the trees, flyin' so hard his feet didn't hardly touch the ground.

Now wasn't he sharp?

'Course, he wasn't so smart to start with, was he, puttin' a blacksnake around his neck? But that's the curious part of it—that the sharpest critter of all got a stupid streak in him some-where. You got to face it, ain't no one got all the wisdom in the world, nor all the stupidity neither.

TERRAPIN'S POT OF SENSE

NOW JUST WHY YOU THINK it is all the critters got different *kinds* of sense, and different amounts too? 'Tain't merely on account of they got a shape like a rabbit or turkey or a water snake. There's somethin' behind it all, and right now it's what I'm goin' to talk about.

In the old days they was a big competition 'mongst the animals to see which one of 'em could collect the most good sense. Buh Coon, Buh Fox, Buh Guinea, Buh Geese, Buh Snake, and all the others went runnin' around pickin' up pieces of good sense on the ground or on the bushes or wherever they could find 'em. Buh Coon had a little pile of good sense in his place, Buh Rabbit had a little pile in his place, Buh Rooster had some in his place. Of course, they was all in such a hurry to outdo the other folks that some of the sense they picked up wasn't so good, and some was downright spoiled. But everyone was braggin' 'bout what a pile of sense he had back home. Trouble was, the places they had to keep it wasn't just right. Buh Possum's house had a leak in the roof, and everytime it rained, the water came drip, drip, drip, down on Possum's pile of sense. Buh 'Gator he put his sense in the nest where he keep his eggs, but every time the young ones

24

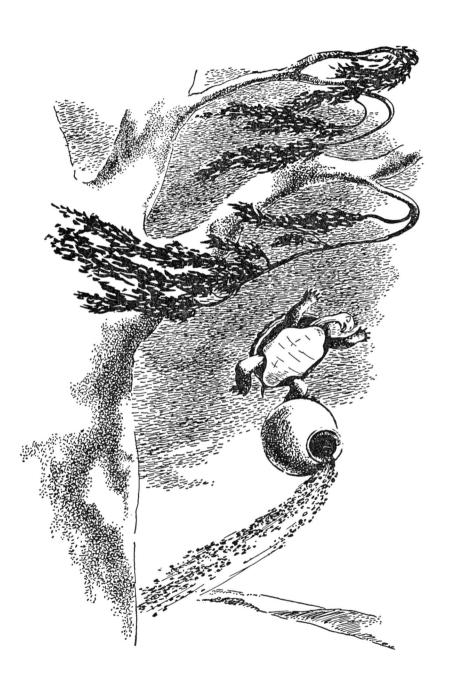

hatch out they jump around and kick the good sense all over the place. Buh Rooster have his good sense in a nice pretty pile, but his wife, Sister Hen she's so nearsighted she can't tell sense from corn, and she was always a-peckin' at it. Buh Duck he want to fly South in the winter and don't know what to do with his pile of sense.

Well, Buh Terrapin he got a fine idea. He say, "Friends, what we need is a caretaker to take care of all the sense we gathered. You just bring it to me and I'll be the caretaker."

All the animals liked that idea, 'cause it eased their worries for 'em. So they all brought the sense they'd collected to Buh Terrapin, and he gave each and every one of 'em a receipt for it. Then he took all that sense and put it in a big iron cookin' pot.

Afterward he begin to study where could he hang the pot. At last he decided he goin' to hang it top of a great big sycamore tree safe and sound. So he took the pot in front of him and went to climb the tree with it. But he got a powerful problem, 'cause the pot was pretty big and Terrapin's legs was too short in the first place to be climbin' trees. Took Terrapin most of the day to get halfway up. All the critters was standin' around watchin' that pot of sense go up, sayin', "Hey there, Buh Terrapin, careful of that pot! It got my sense in it!"

Just afore nightfall a wind come up and begin blowin' things around. The top of the sycamore tree began to switch back and forth. Wind got stronger, and the top of the tree commence to whippin' around till Buh Terrapin couldn't hold on no more. He hollered, "Here I come!" and let go.

Buh Terrapin landed smack on his back and lay right there where he fall. The iron pot hit the ground and rolled this way and that. Naturally, everything that was in it got scattered all over. All the critters started to run around pickin' up pieces of sense. Everything was mixed up, and couldn't no one tell which was his and which was somebody else's. Didn't have time then to figure out what was good sense, or ordinary sense, or plain stupidity—everybody just grabbed.

And when they had they hands full and didn't know what to do with it, Buh Horse say, "I don't know what all you folks doin' with yours, but I'm puttin' mine in my head." And when he did that, the others say, "I'm puttin' mine in my head too," and they did the same as Buh Horse did. That's how come all the critters got sense in their heads. And they got good sense and bad sense as well. Some's luckier than others in what they picked up. Mostly everybody got a mixture, though.

When that part of it was all over, they saw Buh Terrapin still on his back, and they righted him. They saw his shell was all cracked from fallin' on the ground, just the way it's been ever since. They went away and left him. Terrapin he crawled around in the grass lookin' for bits of sense they'd left behind. He found some, but they hadn't left much for him. When you see Buh Terrapin crawlin' around in the grass nowadays, you can figure he's still lookin' for some scraps of sense.

That's a sad story for Buh Terrapin, ain't it? But some folks figure he had it comin', on account of they think he was fixin' to get all the sense for himself by appointin' himself caretaker.

SLOW TRAIN TO ARKANSAS

JUST 'CAUSE Buh Terrapin had last pickin's on the sense that was scattered around doesn't mean he didn't get *anything*. He got himself a little bit here and there, and by puttin' it all together it added up. He had enough of it to help him outsmart Buh Rabbit, and that's somethin' lots of other critters would like to say they'd done.

Buh Terrapin, the slow train to Arkansas, got to talkin' to Buh Rabbit one day, and put on a big bet with him. He say, "Buh Rabbit, you considers yourself a fast runner, don't you? Well, I'll tell you what, I'm goin' to race you from here to the creek and see which one of us is the fastest. And I'll beat, what you think of that?"

"You can't do it," Rabbit say.

"It's three miles to the creek," Terrapin say, "When I count three, light out."

Terrapin counted One, Two, Three. And BAM! Rabbit hit the ground with his back feet and took off.

Now, the way it was, three terrapins had got together and made a plot against Rabbit. First Terrapin stayed right where Buh Rabbit left him. Second Terrapin was halfway down to the creek, and when Buh Rabbit come along he holler, "Here I am, Buh Rabbit, beat you this far anyway, and now I'm goin' to beat you the rest of the way."

Buh Rabbit say, "How you get here so fast? Thought I left you a mile and a half behind." And he lit out for the creek fast as he could make it.

Third Terrapin he was settin' on the creek bank. When he see Buh Rabbit heave into view he holler, "Beat you to the creek, man!" and he jump in the water with a splash.

Buh Rabbit he's might perplexed 'bout this situation. Stood there scratchin' his head and tryin' to figure out how come Buh

Terrapin get there first. "Buh Terrapin," he say, "for a man with such a slow start, you sure got a fast pickup."

Terrapin start crawlin' up on the bank then, and say, "Buh Rabbit, race you back to the place we started, and double the stakes."

"You're on!" Rabbit say. He spin around and take off without waitin' for one, two, three, light out. This time Buh Rabbit was really shovelin' coal. You could hear them back feet of his hit the ground like a gang of men was tampin' railroad ties. Anything he could go over, he went over. When he run around a tree he cut so close he left some of his hair stickin' to the bark. "This time I'm goin' to show Buh Terrapin some *runnin'*," Rabbit say to himself.

'Bout this time Second Terrapin, the one halfway between, had got himself turned around facin' home. When Rabbit came tearin' through the brush, his ears layin' back, really sailin' along, this Terrapin holler, "Here I am, Buh Rabbit! Beat you to the middle!"

Rabbit couldn't hardly believe it, seein' Terrapin there. But he don't stop to make conversation. BAM! His feet hit the ground and this time he really went. What he did now made what he did before look like a lazy walk. Went through the woods like double forked lightnin' carryin' the mail.

By this time First Terrapin had got himself turned around with his nose touchin' the tree where the race started. Rabbit ran another mile and a half and came in with his breath whistlin' in and out of his mouth.

"I'm here!" First Terrapin holler.

When Rabbit hear that and see Terrapin at the finish line, he just quit. "I sure give it to you, Buh Terrapin. You're a faster man than I figured on," Rabbit say.

That's how Buh Terrapin beat Buh Rabbit in a foot race, six miles, three goin' and three comin'. Rabbit nearly run himself to death, and Buh Terrapin ain't moved a step.

BUH RABBIT'S HUMAN WEAKNESS

A HEAD, that's a place to keep your thoughts, ain't it? You study up on things and everything you learn you can keep right in your head. But every time you open your mouth, you got to take care somethin' don't leak out.

It's like the time the animals was havin' a big revival meetin' down in the bottoms. Everyone was there, the rabbits and possums and coons and turkeys and geese. Folks'd come from all over to hear the preachin'; and the singin' and shoutin' went on all night. Four or five preachers was there, and every time one of 'em talked himself out or got too hoarse to carry on, another one jumped up. 'Bout seven in the mornin' all the folks was tuckered out and went home to rest up till nine o'clock.

Well, the preachers was off together in the cornfield restin' up too. Preacher Coon, Preacher Possum, Preacher Dog, Preacher Fox, Preacher Rooster, and Preacher Rabbit, they sat around talkin'. They been talkin' so much all night they couldn't stop.

Preacher Coon he say, "Brothers, all night long we been preachin' about sin and human weakness. When you stop to think on it, ain't hardly a man without *some* kind of weakness, is there? Take me now, I got a weakness. Think I'll confess about my weakness here, 'cause I know it won't go no further. You know, I'm just crazy 'bout apples and grapes. If I'm goin' down

31

the road and sees some fruit growin' in somebody's garden, I can't resist goin' in and takin' a few."

When he hear that, Preacher Dog say, "Brothers, I got a weakness too. Wouldn't say a word about it, but I knows no one going to say a thing. My weakness is stealin' meat. When the man I'm livin' with shoots and quarters a deer, I just can't keep away; and when he ain't lookin', I go down on that meat and eat some of it. It's just my nature."

Well, you know, all the preachers start to confessin' 'bout their weaknesses then, can't hardly wait for their turn.

Preacher Rooster say, "Brothers, I got a bad weakness myself. Every time I sees a chicken I just got to chase her."

Fox he say, "Brothers, me too, I got a bad human weakness. I like to drink. Every time I see a jug of corn liquor I feels like I got to take a little swallow."

'Bout this time it was nine o'clock, and the meetin' was fixin' to start again. Every one of them preachers had confessed 'bout his weakness and sins 'cept Rabbit. He just set there. They asks Buh Rabbit if he didn't have no weaknesses.

He say, "Brothers, I got a human weakness too. It's a real terrible human weakness. It's so bad I just hate to tell you about it. My weakness is gossip; can't never keep anything to myself, and I just can't wait to get out of here!" And BAM! He was gone.

The point of it all is that recognition of your weak points is good for your salvation; but when you makes it a subject of conversation, you got only yourself to blame.

BUH RABBIT'S BIG EAT

ONE CRITTER that always give Buh Rabbit a bad time is Buh Alligator. Buh Alligator he always talkin' real sweet, like, "Good evenin', how's all your folks doin' this evenin'?" And on Sunday Buh 'Gator always sittin' right up front in church prayin' and singin' with the most noise you ever heard. But the way he talks and prays ain't the way he acts. For one thing, he been eatin' Buh Rabbit's young ones, and Rabbit had just about enough of that. So he made a plot against Buh Alligator.

One mornin' he went down to the water where Buh 'Gator was always hangin' around, and say, "Mornin', Mr. Alligator. I came down to talk with you a little bit this mornin'."

Buh 'Gator he say, "What you got on your mind, Buh Rabbit?"

Rabbit say, "You know, we givin' a big eat over here today."

"That so?" Buh 'Gator say. "What you goin' to have for music?"

"Plenty," Buh Rabbit say. "Mr. Mockin'bird goin' to sing; Mr. Wrenbird goin' to sing; Mr. Turkledove goin' to moan, and Mr. Owl goin' to hoot for us. Mr. Turkey goin' to yelp. And Mr. Partridge goin' to sing *Pa-ta-da-humm! Pa-ta-da-humm!* Mockin'-

bird goin' to sing *Treedle-oo! Treedle-oo!* Jaybird goin' to holler *Jay! Jay!* Wrenbird holler, *Hyah! Hyah!* We goin' to get all them folks together to be our music, and they's goin' to be a mighty dance.

"Another thing," Buh Rabbit say, "Mr. Possum goin' to bake paste for us. Mr. Coon goin' to run straight out there, back and forth, and Mr. Fox goin' to run 'round and 'round."

Mr. Alligator say, "That sure sounds like a big jamboree. I want to be in on that. Where's it goin' to be?"

"Right over there in that big straw patch," Rabbit say. "We want to make it right convenient for your whole family, Mr. Alligator. Goin' to have a table for you in that straw patch and you and your folks can just gather 'round it to eat. We goin' to make music down by the creek, give you the whole straw patch for your eatin'.

"Furthermore, we goin' to dance Bertillion," Rabbit say. Rabbit can dance mighty pretty, you know, turn double somersaults and all that. "Mr. Possum goin' to roll on the ground; Mr. Coon goin' to run; Dog goin' to bark and howl down there with pretty music; and birds goin' to be singin' overhead in the air. Mr. Wild Goose say he goin' to cackle mighty. Duck say he goin' to rock and walk and talk for us, so come on and hear all this music!"

Alligator say, "I'm comin' out then!" He commenced crawlin' out of the water with all his family—a big mess of alligators they was. They ganged up and came on up to the straw patch and sat around waitin' for the food and the music and dancin'.

" 'Nother thing," Rabbit say, "we goin' to have fun at the first and Double Trouble on the last. When I holler 'Fun!' you look around and you'll see Double Trouble after it."

"What's this Double Trouble you talkin' about, Buh Rabbit?" Alligator say.

"We're savin' that for a surprise," Rabbit say.

Well, Rabbit he commence to dance Bertillion, *bzz bzz bzz*, like that, and Mr. Alligator and his folks get up and start to dance 'round and 'round too. Like Rabbit say, down by the creek Mr. Dog begin to bark and howl; Mr. Coon begin to run back and forth; Possum roll on the ground; Mockin'bird sing *Treedle-oo! Treedle-oo!* Turkledove moan, and Jaybird holler *Jay! Jay!* Mr. Partridge sing *Humm! Pa-ta-da-humm!* Wrenbird call *Hyah! Hyah!* Crow cawed, Turkey gobbled, Goose cackled, and Duck he rocked and walked and talked. They made mighty music down there, you could almost hear it in Mobile.

And while all this was goin' on, Mr. Alligator and all his folks was dancin' Bertillion, 'round and 'round, waitin' for Rabbit to bring on the victuals.

But 'midst all this noise, Buh Rabbit slipped out with a match and set the whole straw field afire in a big ring around where the alligators was dancin'. In no time at all the smoke was goin' 'up; the birds disappear out of the air; geese stopped cacklin'; everybody stopped singin'; and Mr. Alligator holler, "Fire!"

Buh Rabbit holler, "Fun!"

Alligator holler, "Fire!"

Buh Rabbit holler, "Fun!"

Smoke gettin' blacker all around, and Mr. Alligator holler again, "Fire!"

Rabbit holler, "Fun!"

At last when that ring of fire get too hot, Buh Rabbit skipped off down by the creek.

"Fire!" Buh Alligator holler, runnin' 'round and 'round.

"Double Trouble!" Rabbit call back. "Buh Alligator, you been eatin' up my young 'uns, and now you got your Double Trouble!"

Well, in no time at all you could hear them alligators burning up in the straw patch, poppin' just like canebrake on fire.

And that's what happened when Buh Rabbit had enough of Mr. Alligator preyin' on his young 'uns. Now it don't pay to fool around with Buh Rabbit, does it?

BUH FOX'S NUMBER NINE SHOES

Y OU CHILDREN ever study about how come Buh Rabbit generally get the best of things, particularly with Buh Fox? You'd think Buh Fox goin' to learn a few tricks, the way Rabbit always outsmartin' him. Buh Fox sort of figure it that way too, and that's why he never give up tryin' to out-trick Buh Rabbit. Just about everything Buh Rabbit do in his dealin's with Buh Fox is a little different. He never do the same trick twice, and that's the secret of it. Every time Fox get the worst of it from Rabbit, he say, "Man, I'm goin' to remember that trick. Rabbit ain't *never* goin' to catch me with it again." Well then, next time it's a different trick Rabbit does. Fox is smart enough in his way. He never make the same mistake twice. But just the same, every one of his mistakes has a big resemblance to all the others.

That's the way it was the time Fox had Buh Rabbit holed up in a hollow log. Log had a hole at both ends, but Fox wouldn't go in either way 'cause he's afraid Buh Rabbit go out the other way. So he just set there waitin'. He say, "Buh Rabbit, come on out. Ain't no use hidin' in there, 'cause if you do I'll just starve you to death."

Buh Rabbit say, "I don't know about that, Mr. Fox. Reckon I can wait just as long as you."

So Buh Fox just wait, settin' there in the hot sun with his tongue hangin' out. Rabbit don't mind it where he's at, it's nice and cool in there. Buh Fox commence to get hungry.

After a while Rabbit say, "Mr. Fox, you must get mighty tired eatin' nothin' but rabbit and chicken. How'd you like to try a big mess of fish for a change?"

"Well," Fox say, "what you got on your mind?"

"The way it is," Buh Rabbit say, "Buh Bear went fishin' this mornin', and pretty soon he's comin' home with a cartful. Man, it sure makes my mouth water."

"Mine too," Fox say, "but you made a big fool of me before, Buh Rabbit, and I ain't takin' no chances. Besides, ain't nobody can get them fish away from Buh Bear."

" 'Cept me," Rabbit say, "But if you don't want to go partners on this trick, don't make no difference to me. I got a big pile of greens in here and I'm fixed to stay a couple of weeks."

"I'll tell you what," Buh Fox say. "You come on out and we'll get the fish."

Buh Rabbit say, "How I know you ain't foolin' me, Buh Fox? I think I'm goin' to hole up here for a while."

"Come on, Rabbit," Fox say. "You got my mouth waterin' for fish."

So Buh Rabbit come out of the log. He say, "You stay here in the bushes and keep quiet. I'll go down the road a ways and wait for Buh Bear."

Fox he suspicious what Rabbit goin' to do, but he set in the bushes while Rabbit went down the road. When Rabbit see Buh Bear comin' along with his load of fish, he took off one of his shoes and set it right in the middle of the road, and then he hid himself in the grass. Pretty soon Buh Bear get there hollerin' giddap to his mule. When he see that one lonesome shoe there in the road he stop. "That shoe might just fit me," Bear say, "but what good is one shoe?" After that he left the shoe where it was and went on his way with his cartload of fish.

Well, Buh Rabbit take that shoe, the very same one, and run

way 'round the field till he get ahead of Buh Bear again, and he put the shoe back in the road. When Buh Bear get there he say, "What you know, there's the other one!" And he left the cart right where it was and went back to get the first shoe.

Soon as he's gone, Buh Rabbit put his shoe on and take all the fish out of Buh Bear's cart. He gave some to Buh Fox and headed home with all the rest.

Now Buh Fox see everything that Buh Rabbit do. "That's a mighty smart trick," he say, "I think I can do it myself." So next day he wait for Buh Bear to come along with a load of fish, and he put one of his own shoes, number nine, out in the road where Buh Bear will see it. Buh Bear he been fooled once, but he been doin' some thinkin' since he lost all his fish the day before. So when he see Buh Fox's shoe, he pick it up and throw it in the cart. Don't wait to find the other one.

Buh Fox he run way ahead of the cart, and of course he's only got one shoe left now, so he puts that one in the road and wait for Mr. Bear to come along. Naturally there wasn't no purpose in it any more, but Buh Fox didn't get the point of it. When Buh Bear come along, he stop just long enough to pick up the other shoe.

"Well, now, I got a mighty fine pair of number nines," Bear say. "Giddap, mule."

Fox find out he's got no shoes at all, and no fish either. So he run after Bear, sayin', "Mornin', Buh Bear. You happen to find a nice pair of shoes this mornin'?"

"Maybe I did," Buh Bear say. "What size you wear?"

"Number nine," Fox say.

"I learned a lot about shoes since yesterday," Bear say, "Come on here and tell me are these shoes yours."

"Yeah, they sure look like my shoes, Buh Bear," Fox say.

"Look close," Bear say.

Buh Fox put his nose right up there. "They're mine all right," he say.

Bear grab Fox by the scruff of the neck. "You got my fish yesterday, Buh Fox," he say, "and I got you today!"

Well, the whuppin' Bear gave Buh Fox was a sight to see. Fox yelpin' and hollerin', Buh Bear cuffin' him first on one side then the other, and red fur flyin' every-which-way. When Fox got out of there he was a sad sight. Had to go home and grow a new coat of fur, and ain't *nobody* see him for four weeks and seven days.

Like I said before, the moral is—it don't do you no good to learn the right trick at the wrong time. Trouble with Buh Fox, if he'd done that trick on *Wednesday* 'stead of *Thursday* he'd made good on it. *Time* is one element you can't fool around with.

BUH RABBIT'S TAIL

LIKE I TOLD YOU BEFORE, just about everybody got a mixture of good sense. What I mean, take Buh Rabbit. He's about the smartest critter there is, but he ain't *only* got good sense, he got some bad judgment mixed in with it.

There was that time he got stuck to the tar man. You remember, he was stealin' corn from Buh Possum's field, and Buh Possum put up the tar man in it. When Buh Rabbit come that night to steal some corn, he saw that tar man in the moonlight and made a fuss with him. He say, "Man, get out of this field which belongs to Buh Possum afore I give you what for." That tar man couldn't talk, of course, and that made Buh Rabbit mad. So he give him a slap with his right hand and it stuck. You'd think that would rouse a little good sense in Buh Rabbit's mind, wouldn't you? But it don't. It stir up the meanness and stupidity in him. So he give the tar man another slap with his left hand, and that stuck too. Then he kick him with his right foot and his left foot. And when he was all stuck by hands and feet, he could have stopped to think about the way it was. But he didn't. No, sir, not Buh Rabbit. All he think about was that field of corn he was goin' to eat. So he give the tar man a squeeze and got his

41

belly stuck. Then he give a butt with his head, and that stuck too.

Now you see what I mean? Buh Rabbit was mighty smart before, when he was stealin' corn. And he was mighty smart afterward, when he got Buh Possum and the other folks to throw him in the brier patch 'stead of killin' him. But right smack in the middle of that smartness he lost his head and was just as stupid as he could be. There's lots of reasons a smart man loses his sense. Sometimes it's 'cause he's too proud of himself.

Now, take the time Buh Fox got Buh Rabbit holed up in a hollow tree. This time Buh Rabbit had been eatin' corn out of Fox's garden, and Buh Fox took out after Rabbit and run him up into this hollow tree, right on the bank of the river. Fox kept runnin' around and around the tree, and every time he'd look up to see where Rabbit was, Buh Rabbit would throw trash down in his eyes. All the time this goin' on, Buh Bullfrog was sittin' on the edge of the river watchin' the goin's-on.

Buh Bullfrog say, "Buh Fox, you ain't goin' to get him by runnin' around that way. Why don't you get you a long stick and twist him out of there?"

So Buh Fox got him a long stick and poked it up in the tree to twist Rabbit out, but Rabbit kept catchin' hold of the stick and breakin' the end off.

"I'll tell you what," Buh Bullfrog say. "Whyn't you go home and get your ax and chop that tree down? Then you can split it open with your ax and get him."

Buh Fox say, "Well, it's a good idea, but it's too far to run. I got to run three miles goin' and three miles comin', and I'm already tired. Listen here, Buh Bullfrog, how much you charge me to sit down here and watch Buh Rabbit so's he don't hop down and get away while I'm gone?"

"I'll charge you five dollars," Buh Bullfrog say, "and I'll guarantee you he'll be there when you get back."

"All right," Fox say, "I'll pay you when I get back."

"No, you better pay me before you go," Bullfrog say. "You might fool me."

So Fox count out five dollars and give it to Bullfrog. Buh Bullfrog hop off the bank right under the tree, lookin' straight up into it.

"I got him," Bullfrog say, "I'm lookin' right at him."

So Fox lit out to get his ax, three miles to go and three more to get back.

When Fox was gone a mile or more, Buh Rabbit reached in his back pocket and took out a plug of tobacco and chewed it. Then he aimed and spit tobacco juice right into Bullfrog's eyes. Bullfrog hollered, "Look!" and struck the water. When Buh Bullfrog struck the water, Buh Rabbit crawled out of the tree. "Good-by, Buh Bullfrog," Buh Rabbit hollered, "I'm gone!"

When Buh Bullfrog got the tobacco juice washed out of his eyes, he came out of the water and sat by the tree like Buh Rabbit was still there. Didn't want to make Buh Fox mad. When Buh Fox got back a-runnin' with his ax, Bullfrog was still settin' there, lookin' up into the tree with his big eyes.

"Hurry," Bullfrog say, "that sun is burnin' my eyes."

When Fox start to cut down the tree, Buh Bullfrog say, "Don't reckon you need me now, he's all yours. Goin' back in the water to cool my eyes off." He hollered, "Look!" and he jumped in the river.

Buh Fox cut and cut, and he cut the tree down. Then he split it open and stood lookin'. "I don't see no Buh Rabbit," he say, "all I see is his hair. I think you fooled me, Buh Bullfrog."

"Listen," Bullfrog say, "if Rabbit had done to you what he done to me, you'd have sold out yourself. He spit a plug of tobacco in my eyes and I had to get in the water to wash it off."

Buh Fox was outsmarted by Buh Rabbit and Buh Bullfrog both, and he don't like it. So he went off and hid in his garden for Buh Rabbit to come back and eat some more corn. You'd think Rabbit would have learned somethin', but sure enough in no time at all he was back again. And he looked over that garden and stood up and say, "Wonder will I have watermelon or corn today?" Just then Fox jumped at him and say, "Don't know what *you* havin' today, but *I'm* havin' rabbit stew."

Rabbit lit out again, with Fox right on his tail. This time Fox was real mad, and he don't let Rabbit gain an inch on him. Rabbit go north, Fox right there with him. Rabbit turn south, Fox turn south. East and west, it's all the same, Fox was just a couple of lengths behind. Rabbit tried the brush, but Fox stayed with him. Rabbit tried the open field, but Fox came right along.

Pretty soon Rabbit say, "Man, I'm givin' out. If I don't get somewhere soon, I'm rabbit stew." Just then he come to a small hole in the ground and squeezed himself in. Hole was too small for Fox, he couldn't get in. Buh Rabbit just lay there, his tongue hangin' out, catchin' his breath. After a while he commence to feel better, and say to himself, "I sure outrun Mr. Fox that time." 'Course, Rabbit ain't figurin' to get out of that hole for a long while. He commence to talk to himself. He see one of his big ears hangin' over his eye, and say, "Ear, you sure done me good. You hear Fox comin' along behind me and helped me steer my course." He looked at his hind legs and say, "Legs, you sure done good, pushin' and hoppin' this way and that." Then he looked at his tail.

Now in those days Rabbit had a long tail, not a short one. 'Bout as long as a dog's tail, it was. He looked at his long white tail switchin' back and forth, and his face got dark. He say, "Tail, you was just about the ruination of me. Here I am runnin', for my life, and what do you do? Just stretch right out straight behind me ticklin' Fox's nose. All the time everything else I got was workin' together to get me out of trouble, there you were wavin', 'Come on,' to Mr. Fox. Now you acts like one of the family. Well, you ain't. You can get right out of this hole. Go on, scat! Ain't no room for you here!"

Buh Rabbit turned himself around and backed up to the opening of that hole and pushed his tail right out.

Of course Buh Fox been waitin' outside, and when he saw that tail comin' out, whack!—he clamped his teeth on it. He pulled, and Buh Rabbit clawed. It was a mighty tug of war. A time came when that tail parted in two. Buh Rabbit was a sorrowful sight. He crawled further down in the hole and stayed there a good long time. Fox say, "I didn't get Rabbit, but I sure got his tail."

Since that time Buh Rabbit hasn't had hardly no tail at all, just a ball of cotton, like you see it.

That was the time the mixture of good sense was runnin' mighty lean in Buh Rabbit. Once in a while he looks at his short tail and gets a powerful message of wisdom from it.

THE WELL

ONE TIME the rivers and lakes and everything dried up on account of there wasn't no rain. You might say it was the worst dry spell they ever had, and it was gettin' mighty difficult even to get a drink of water anywhere. So all the animals got together in a big meetin' to discuss the situation.

"It's sure bad for me and my family," Buh 'Gator say, "we ain't got no water to crawl in, and we can't take this hot sun."

"We're worse off than you," Buh Catfish say, "we floppin' around in the mudholes and pretty soon they goin' to be altogether dried up, the way things are goin'."

Buh Wasp say, "Where's that mud at? I'm lookin' for a little bit of wet mud to make my nest out of, but can't find it. Everything turn to sand around my place."

"Never mind about these particulars," Buh Coon say, "the main problem is what we goin' to drink. Anybody got any suggestions?"

"Milk," Buh Calf holler, "I goin' to drink milk."

"No, you ain't," Sister Cow say. "If I don't get no water soon, you ain't goin' to have no milk neither."

"What we got to have is a well," Buh Coon say. "Everybody want to drink water can help dig it."

Right then and there everybody went to work. There was some powerful diggers 'mongst them animals. Mr. Ground Hog, he's a natural-born digger. So's Mr. Mole. Sister Chicken scratched away. Buh Bull pawed the ground. Buh Horse kicked up the dirt. Buh Dog had lots of experience, and he went to it with his two front feet, stickin' his nose down in the hole every once in a while to see could he smell water. Buh Worm wriggled down and loosened the dirt. Buh Crow come down and picked up the loose stones and flew off with 'em. Mr. Fox, he's a diggin' man too, and he pitched in. Only one of all those animals didn't join in the diggin'. That was Buh Rabbit. He just set off to one side in the shade, watchin' the rest of 'em work.

After a while Buh Coon say, "Mr. Rabbit, how come you ain't diggin' with the rest of us?"

Rabbit, he say, "I don't need no well for myself, Buh Coon. I can lick the dew off the grass, that's plenty water for me."

"Well, there's one thing about it," Coon say, "ain't *nobody* drinks from this well but the ones who *digs* it."

"Yeah," the other critters say, "if Buh Rabbit ain't goin' to dig, he can't have no water."

After a while they hit water gravel, and the water came and filled up the hole. Let me tell you, all them animals was real happy with that. Everybody what wanted a drink came and took it. Buh Wasp took some water off and made some mud of his own and went to work buildin' his nest. Buh Catfish hauled some water off in a pail and poured it in the mudhole where his young ones was livin'. Alligator took some and splashed it on himself to cool off.

Next mornin' when they came back again, they find Buh Rabbit's tracks there. This makes all the folks real mad, 'cause Rabbit ain't done nothin' toward the diggin' of that well. They say, "What we need is a watchman to keep Mr. Rabbit away." So they 'pointed Buh Bear watchman. When night come, Buh Bear sat down by the well and waited. Buh Rabbit hidin' in the bushes, but he don't come out. After a while Buh Bear fall asleep. Then Rabbit come and get a drink and go away.

In the mornin' the animals come and say, "You seen Buh Rabbit last night?"

"Uh-uh, I ain't seen 'im," Bear say.

"Man, you must have been asleep," they say. "There's his tracks."

Next night they 'point Buh Wolf as watchman, but he fall asleep too. In the mornin' they find Buh Rabbit's tracks again.

"Seems to me we got to have somethin' better," Buh Coon tell all the folks. "I recommend we 'lect Buh Bullfrog as watchman."

"Me too," the animals holler, and they made Bullfrog the watchman.

That night Bullfrog sit by the well, watchin' with them big round eyes. Every time his eyes begin to close he holler, "I'm gone!" and jump in the water to freshen himself up.

Every time Rabbit think the watchman is asleep, he begin to creep up on the well, and Bullfrog holler, "Here he is! Here he is!"

Then Rabbit got to skedaddle to the bushes again.

Now I ask you, you ever see a rabbit drinkin' at the well? You sure don't, and you never will. And you ever figure why there's a frog in every well? He's the watchman, that's why, and he keeps Rabbit away. Almost every night you can hear Bullfrog holler, "Here he is! Here he is!" Or once in a while he says, "I'm gone!" and jumps in the water to wake himself up. That's the reason we got frogs in wells, and it's the main reason Buh Rabbit got to get up real early in the mornin' and lick the dew off the grass, like he boasted he could do.

There's just one more point about all this. I guess you never give much studyin' to why that long-handled pump out there screeches like anything sometimes, and other times it don't. Fact is, it pick up from where Buh Bullfrog left off. Every time it screeches when you pump it, that's because Buh Rabbit is loiterin' around waitin' to get a drink. If you listen good you can hear what that screech say—"Quit hangin' around! Quit hangin' around!"

Point is, no matter how sharp you are, you got to keep on the good side of people, else your smart ways goin' to get you in difficulty. There's a lot to bein' sharp, and maybe you can use it against one critter at a time and come off good, but when it comes to bein' sharp against the whole community at once, it don't pay off.

RABBIT SCRATCHES BUH ELEPHANT'S BACK

THERE WAS THAT TIME Buh Wolf was after Buh Rabbit. Wolf claim Rabbit was eatin' his young ones. Course, everyone knows rabbits don't eat meat, but every time Mr. Wolf or Mr. Fox or Mr. 'Gator want an excuse against Buh Rabbit, they claim he been eatin' their children. It's the way it is with lots of folks 'round here, givin' to other folks their own worst faults.

Anyway, Buh Wolf got Rabbit's scent and was after him. Rabbit wasn't gainin' no ground neither. Wolf he's pretty fast when he's hungry, you know. Well, Buh Rabbit gettin' kind of scared he goin' to give out. And right then he come to where Buh Elephant was in the jungle. Buh Elephant he didn't seem to notice Rabbit. He was havin' a big time tryin' to scratch his back, one particular spot on his back that he couldn't reach with his trunk. First he rub against the big trees, but he can't reach the place that itches him. Then he roll on the ground, but that's a big operation for an elephant. Then he pick up trash and stuff with his trunk and throw it on his back. But nothin' didn't seem to do him no good.

Buh Rabbit takin' it all in. He say, "Mornin', Mr. Elephant."

Elephant say, "Mornin', but it sure feels more like evenin' to me, my back itches so bad."

Rabbit say, "Expect I could help you some, Mr. Elephant. Hoist me on your back and I'll scratch for you."

"Well, you sure is a friend," Elephant say, and he pick up Rabbit with his trunk and put him up there on top of him. "Right there in the middle, back of the ears," he says.

"All right," Rabbit say, "only thing is, when I scratch, you got to holler and trumpet like you was dyin'. You hear?"

"Sure, sure, I hear, only get on with the scratchin'," Elephant say.

Rabbit he start scratchin' with his feet, then he nibble with his teeth. Buh Elephant moan with pleasure.

"Holler," Buh Rabbit say.

So Elephant holler, "Oh, oh! You killin' me! I'm dyin'!" Then he put up his trunk and trumpet a big blast.

Just about then old Buh Wolf come along. He hear Buh Elephant carryin' on, and say, "Wonder what's the matter?" He crawl along a little on his belly and poke his nose through the bushes. There was Buh Elephant stampin' back and forth on the ground, swingin' his head this way and that way, hollerin' like he's bein' killed. And right on top of him was Buh Rabbit, kickin' and bitin' and scratchin'. Buh Wolf's eyes 'bout popped out of his head lookin' at that sight. He just froze to the ground.

When Rabbit see Wolf, he begin to cavort twice as bad as before. "I'm hungry and I'm mad!" he hollered. "Goin' to finish off this here meat and then I'm goin' after Buh Wolf, 'cause he been sniffin' my trail and that makes me lose my temper!"

Wolf hear that, he turn around and head the way he come, kickin' up the dust and breathin' hard. "Let me out of here," he say. "I'm on my way!"

Now ain't that Rabbit sharp?

BUH MOUSE TESTIFIES

SOMETIMES IT GETS pretty sorrowful the way animals and humanfolks have got it in for each other. Somebody is always turnin' on somebody else, and like as not it's somebody smaller. It reminds me of the time there was a meetin' of all the animals to talk about why things were goin' so bad all over. Things were mighty sad that year. Corn was only growin' knee-high, boll weevil ate up most all the cotton, rain didn't fall, wells dried up, and didn't nothin' go right. All kinds of animals was at the meetin'— Fox, Lion, Alligator, Coon, Possum, Dog, Bear, Turkey, Guinea, and all the rest.

Well, Buh Coon he call the meetin' to order and ask does anyone know why things ain't goin' so good. Some animals say this, some say that, and it all boil down to the fact that somebody committed a bad sin and made the Lord angry with 'em.

"The way it looks," Buh Coon say, "we all got to confess our sins and repent, and the ones who really done bad got to be punished."

So everyone got to tellin' 'bout the bad things he done.

Buh Alligator say, "I crawled out of the water one day and ate up Buh Rabbit's young ones." Whilst talkin', Buh Alligator roll his eyes around at Buh Possum, Sister Chicken, Mr. Turkey, and Buh Guinea like he still hungry. When they see Alligator with that mean look, they holler, "No sir, Buh Alligator, that ain't no sin. A man got to eat, and that's a fact. Don't rack your head no more about it."

Grizzly Bear's turn then, and he say, "I been stealin' honey left and right, trompin' down folks' berry patches and eatin' their berries. I really done wrong. I give quite a few folks a bad time. I'm mean-tempered too. I cuffed Mr. Dog a good one when he came sniffin' around my place. Ate quite a few of Buh Hog's young ones too." All the time he sayin' that, Buh Bear showin' his teeth and his red eyes at everyone. And they all holler back, "No sir, Buh Bear, ain't nothin' wrong with your behavior. Don't let it worry you."

Then 'twas Buh Lion's turn. All the time he's testifyin' to the bad things he done, he's switchin' his tail back and forth, lookin' at Buh Rabbit and Buh Chicken and the other folks like he ain't had his breakfast yet. "I been *real* bad," he say. "I been eatin' just about everybody's young ones. Reckon Buh Deer recollects how I ate some of his family yesterday, and Sister Cow been makin' quite a few complaints about me in the same connection. Would of had Buh Horse's colt this mornin' but he outran me. Seems to me I'm givin' other folks a sorry time of it."

Buh Deer, Buh Rooster, Buh Terrapin, and the other little animals see Buh Lion's red tongue hangin' out and his big claws goin' in and out, and they all holler, "Uh-uh, Buh Lion, you ain't done bad at all!"

Buh Rattlesnake he's the next one. He say, "I'm the one that's really mean. Other folks act up when they're hungry, but I just go around bitin' everyone for the meanness of it." All the time he's confessin' his sins, Buh Rattlesnake coilin' himself around, flickin' his little tongue in and out, and shakin' his tail. When they see that, everybody includin' Buh Lion and Buh Grizzly Bear replies, "No, no, that ain't really meanness you talkin' about, Buh Rattlesnake, it's just your nature, that's all. Folks got to act 'cordin' to their nature."

Well, that's the way it went along. Buh Dog say he's stealin' meat and chasin' the cat. Buh Bull say he's always hookin' at other folks with his horns. Buh Hawk say he eatin' chickens and rabbits. And after a while it's Buh Mouse's turn.

Buh Mouse say, "Brothers, I been doin' some pretty bad things too. If I go through a field and find a kernel of corn on the ground, I pick it up and take it home for my young ones to eat. When it's time to make a nest, I use anything I can find—straw, old rags layin' around the barnyard, feathers, dried grass, and bits of paper. One year I even took home an old snakeskin, chewed it up in small soft pieces, and used that to make my nest."

When all the animals heard that, they just stopped talkin'. Everybody looked at Buh Mouse, shakin' their heads and cluckin' their tongues like they never heard anything so miserable and mean.

"Look to me like we found the culprit," one of 'em say, and all the others holler, "Yeah, Buh Mouse is the one, he's the sinner that's responsible for everything!"

Then they all jump at Buh Mouse, figurin' to punish him for their hard times. But 'fore they catch him, Buh Mouse sold out, gone in the tall grass.

Now I ask you, ain't that a sorry sight, people actin' that way? The point of it is, the one with the smallest teeth goin' to get the blame for anything that happens. Like the man who got kicked by the mule. He didn't say a word to the mule, but he went right home and whupped his dog, hollerin', "Dog, how many times I got to tell you, keep them hind hoofs of yours on the ground where they belong!"

BUH RABBIT'S GRAVEYARD

BUH BABBIT, now, he's had good days and bad days. On the bad days, ain't nothin' he could do to make things come out right. Like folks say, when things is goin' wrong, even a goose feather can break your head. But when things is good, Rabbit ain't have no trouble at all with his trickin'—come one, come all. Sometimes it 'pears he don't even have to study up on what his tricks is goin' to be, it come so natural.

There was the time Buh Rabbit got together to make a garden with Buh Coon. First thing Buh Coon say is, "Buh Rabbit, how we goin' to share?" And Buh Rabbit say, "Buh Coon, don't let that worry you. You are the biggest and strongest, and you ain't takin' the smallest part, I tell you that." So the two of 'em plow up the field and plant 'tatoes and yams and watermelon and plant them a nice garden. Time comes when all their crops is ready, and Buh Rabbit and Buh Coon fixin' to share. Whilst they're in the watermelon patch, Buh Coon look up the road and see Buh Lion-comin'. "Hey, Buh Rabbit, run for your life!" he holler. "Buh Lion is comin', and he's mean and hungry!"

Buh Coon run for the nearest tree and climb to the topmost branches. Buh Rabbit can't climb, you know, and he didn't know

which way he was a-goin'. He see two watermelon settin' in a
row, and he quick throw some dirt on 'em. Covered 'em all over
with dirt and patted it down, made it look like two fresh graves.
Then he pick up the spade and commence to dig a hole further
down the row.

When Buh Lion get there, he see two fresh graves in a row
and Buh Rabbit diggin' another one. He get mighty curious what's
goin' on there in that garden, and he call out to Rabbit, "Hey,
what kind of buryin' ground is this?"

Buh Rabbit don't even turn around. He talk like he's mad,
say, "Man, there's lot of folks 'round here I can't stand. I gets mean
all over every time I think on 'em. I'm makin' up this graveyard
for all the ones I killed. First grave there, that's where I buried
Buh Alligator. Second one in the row is Buh Bear. Now I got Buh
Coon treed up there, and soon as I get this grave done I goin' to
kill Buh Coon and throw him in."

Buh Lion was plain stupefied, hearin' all this. He look up in
the tree, and sure enough there was Buh Coon shiverin' and
shakin'. Lion could even hear Buh Coon's teeth knockin' together.
Coon was sure scared.

Buh Rabbit begin to holler like he was fit to bust. "You just
hang around a few minutes," he say to Lion. "Soon as I get Buh
Coon put away, I'll dig one for you, 'cause I need a few more
graves to finish out this here row!"

When Buh Lion hear that, he pull his head down and make
himself look small and run down the road like he's carryin' the
mail.

Coon come down out of the tree and shake Buh Rabbit's
hand. He's mighty glad Rabbit so smart.

"Buh Coon," Rabbit say, "how come you left me that way
when Buh Lion come along? You know I can't climb no trees."

"Buh Rabbit," Coon say, "when I see Buh Lion comin', my
feet done all the rest. Didn't even know where I was till I got
there. Anyway, how we goin' to share the crops now?"

"Well, Buh Coon," Rabbit say, "you are the biggest and the

strongest, so you get first pick. The way we share is like this: you take all you can carry away, and me, I just got to accept what's left."

Coon, he liked that mighty fine. "Yeah," he say, "that's the way it's got to be, 'cause I'm the biggest and strongest." He pick up three-four watermelon, and that's all he could take. They was about killin' him they was so heavy, but he toted 'em on home.

Buh Rabbit, he took all the rest—'tatoes, yams, corn, and everything.

Seems like he fixed both Buh Lion and Buh Coon the same day, and didn't have to run a step to do it. Didn't have to outrun 'em. He out talked 'em.

BUH RABBIT AND THE KING

NOW ONE TIME Buh Rabbit tell all the animals he's fixin' tu get himself a wife. When they hear that, they say, "Sorry, Mr. Rabbit, our daughters got previous plans." You see, ain't none of the animals want to give him their daughters 'cause he's always trickin' 'em.

Buh Fox say, "My daughter is already spoken for." Sister Cow say, "My daughter's too young." Buh Coon say, "Buh Rabbit you sure a handsome man, but my daughters has got their mind set on some boys over in Mobile." Buh Porcupine say, "Ain't it too bad, though, 'cause I got nothin' but boy children." Sister Mouse say, "My daughters is fixin' to go up north somewhere." Buh Crow come right out with, "I don't think my daughters wants to marry no Rabbit."

Buh Rabbit don't seem to mind. He tell all them animals, "I ain't fixin' to marry with no girl around here. I got my eye on one over by Meridian. She's a Princess, that's the kind I'm lookin' for."

So he got dressed up real pretty in his best black suit and went to Meridian to see the King over there.

"Mornin', Buh King," he say. "Expect you heard of me. I'm Buh Rabbit and I'd like to get married with your daughter."

Well, this King wasn't lettin' *his* daughter go off and marry just *anyone*. Buh Rabbit was too forward for him. "What make you think you can be the husband of a Princess?" he say. "What you got on you that's special?"

"Well, for one thing I'm real good at outsmartin' folks," Buh Rabbit say. "I got a big name for things like that. Also, I can dance; Waltz and Bertillion, I can sing pretty good, and I'm a mighty runner too, you know."

"The man goin' to be my daughter's husband got to know how to do *plenty* things," King say, "and before I tell you yes or no, I got to find out just how smart you are. You got to bring me two things I need. First thing I want is a bag full of blackbirds. Next thing I want after that is two teeth from a rattlesnake, a live one, you understand. After that is something else you got to do, number three. I'll tell you about that when you get the first two."

"What you want is easy for a smart man like me," Buh Rabbit say. "Old King, you just be here tomorrow mornin' at nine o'clock and I'll meet you. Don't be late, 'cause I'm a man that gets places on time."

Rabbit he ran right home and got him a potato bag. After that he went out in the grove where the blackbirds hung out, and he commenced talkin' to himself like this: "My, oh my, the quails is sure heavier, the quails is sure heavier." Whilst he was talkin' to himself the blackbirds came down and sat in the trees, wonderin' what in the world Rabbit was talkin' about.

"What you sayin' about the quails, Buh Rabbit?" they ask him.

"I just been talkin' to the folks yonder," Buh Rabbit say. "We had a big discussion about which was heaviest, quails or blackbirds. I say it's the quails."

Blackbirds get mad when they hear that. "Uh-uh, you're wrong about that, Buh Rabbit. Blackbirds is got a lot more to 'em than quails. Quails ain't nothin' but breath and feathers."

"Who I goin' to believe?" Rabbit say. "Quails tell me *they* is the heaviest. We never goin' to know 'less we weigh you on the scale. You want to make a test of it?"

"Sure," blackbirds say, "go ahead."

"All right," Rabbit say, "get in the bag and I'll weigh you." He opened the bag up, and the blackbirds started droppin' off the trees like acorns and flyin' right in. In a few minutes it was full to the top. Buh Rabbit closed it up and tied it tight. "I'll be back in an hour, Buh Blackbirds," he say. "I'm off on other business." Then he went lookin' for Buh Rattlesnake. Buh Rattlesnake was sunnin' himself on a stone pile.

"Mornin', Mr. Rattlesnake," Buh Rabbit say. "Don't disturb yourself. I just came around to see if it was so."

"Is *what* so?" Rattlesnake say.

"Oh, folks over in Meridian is sayin' you got a crooked back. I ain't never noticed that before and I come to take a look."

"Ain't nothin' crooked about my back," Buh Rattlesnake say. "I likes to keep it curled, though. Makes it easier to hit out at folks that try to bother me."

"Don't expect you could really straighten out straight," Buh Rabbit say. "You keep curled so much it made you a little crooked."

"You're makin' me mad," Rattlesnake say. "Ain't I told you it's straight?"

"Straighten out a minute," Rabbit say. "Let me take a good look so's I can go back and tell the folks in Meridian."

Buh Rattlesnake crawl off the stone pile onto flat ground and straighten himself out. "How's that look, Buh Rabbit?"

"Straight in front and straight behind," Rabbit say, "but you got a crook in the middle."

"You mean it?" Rattlesnake say.

"Yeah, but I can fix it," Rabbit say. "How you like me to put a splint on you for two-three minutes and straighten you out?"

"I'd be much obliged," Rattlesnake say. "I don't want no crooks in the middle."

"Just lay there for a minute," Rabbit say. He went off and cut a long pole from a tree. He put it on the ground right next to Buh Rattlesnake and tied his tail to it. "Now stretch yourself out, Buh Rattlesnake," he say.

Buh Rattlesnake stretch as far as he can go. Then Buh Rabbit fix to tie Rattlesnake's head to the pole.

"Hey," Buh Rattlesnake say. "What you doin'?"

"Just got to hold you straight with this pole for a minute," Rabbit say.

"Well, come on, get it over with," Buh Rattlesnake say.

Rabbit tied Buh Rattlesnake's neck to the pole. Rattlesnake couldn't bend or curl or move an inch one way or the other. "Ouch, you chokin' me, Buh Rabbit, hurry up," he say.

Rabbit took a pinchers out of his pocket and jumped around with it.

"Hey, Buh Rabbit, what you doin' with those pinchers?" Rattlesnake holler.

"What's wrong with you ain't your back," Rabbit say. "Trouble is you got too many teeth."

And 'fore Rattlesnake knew what was comin', Buh Rabbit pulled out the two big teeth in the front of Rattlesnake's mouth.

"Thanks Buh Rattlesnake," Rabbit say, "and now I'll be gettin' on."

Next mornin' ten before nine he was knockin' on the King's door. "Buh King," he say, "I got your bag of blackbirds and the teeth from Buh Rattlesnake. Now bring your pretty daughter and we'll get married."

"Just a minute," King say, "you got the blackbirds and the rattlesnake teeth, but you still got number three to do. I got this big bag here I want you to take over to that new ground and bury it for me. It's got some money in it and I want it hid in a safe place."

"I'll take care of that in two-three minutes," Buh Rabbit say. "Don't go away, I'm comin' right back." He took the bag the King gave him and toted it out on the new ground.

"If I'm goin' to marry the King's daughter, I ought to get a new suit," Rabbit say. "Don't expect Buh King would mind if I took three-four dollars out of all this money, 'cause I'm practically his son-in-law."

Right then Buh Rabbit untied the bag. There wasn't no money in it at all. What was inside was two of the King's biggest huntin' dogs. Rabbit didn't wait to see any more. "So long," he holler, "I'm gone!" He went across that field so fast his feet didn't hardly touch the ground, headed for Tuscaloosa. The dogs run him across the new ground into the woods, snappin' at his heels all the way to the swamp. If Rabbit would have had a tail, they'd have caught it with their teeth, they were so close. But Rabbit had already lost his tail, so that's what saved him. You see, sometimes there's a virtue in *not* havin' somethin' as well as in *havin'* it.

And that's how come Buh Rabbit didn't ever marry up with no King's daughter.

THE TEXAS
SANDSTORM

MAYBE YOU never stopped to study about how things is so good with us now. We all got shoes in this family, from number four to eleven. They's plenty of canned goods on the pantry shelf, and we got two teams of mules. What I'm goin' to tell you is how it all started.

I was drivin' a herd of cows 'cross the state of Texas one time, and I heard a roarin' comin' up behind me. I say to folks, "What's that roarin' I hear?"

"That's a sandstorm," folks say, "a real Texas sandstorm."

"I heard of them Texas sandstorms," I say, "and I'm goin' to be on my way."

So I jumped on my horse, turned the cattle east, and run 'em as fast as they could go toward Louisiana, figurin' that a Texas storm is a kind of trouble which don't cross state lines. Nonetheless, 'twasn't no time at all till that storm was right on top of us. Sky was black as night, and sand so thick you could climb it right in the air.

My mind got mighty busy then, children. I said to myself, " 'Tain't no use of gettin' destroyed in a sandstorm, 'cause I got a storm pit right in my mouth." What I'm talking 'bout is a great big hollow tooth. I rode my horse around in a big circle, hovered all the cows—a hundred head of 'em, no less—and I drove 'em all into my mouth into that hollow tooth. I didn't want to leave the horse out there in the storm, so I snatched the saddle off him and drove him in after the cows. Then I chunked the saddle in, and jumped in my own self.

Stayed in that hollow tooth till the sandstorm was over with, two months later. When I came out and looked around, I discovered how bad it had been. It never did get into Louisiana, but when it came up against the Louisiana line it pushed the line forty miles east. Folks say Texas sandstorms been doin' that for a long time, and that's the main reason Texas is so big.

Well, the cows bein' in my hollow tooth so long, they rested and fattened up there. One of 'em mind you, just one, she was so big that she had enough meat on her to feed the family for seven years. The skin I took off that cow kept us in shoes from number four to number eleven for twelve years, 'nough for eight children. The first shoe I made never got worn by no one. When I finished it, 'twas still growin', and when it stopped growin' I lived in it ten years for a house till I could make a good wood buildin'. I took one eye from that cow and hung it up for a 'lectric light. And the bones, I used them for fence posts, enough to fence in sixty acres of ground.

And that's why for the next twenty years me and my folks done so well. We been rich ever since.

Now you can quit lookin' in my mouth. If you're looking for the hollow tooth, it ain't there no more. The government sent a expedition down here to get that tooth for a monument. They pulled it out and sent it to Washingon, D.C. Uses it for a regular old meetin' hall. Course, they had to build pretty stout foundations. Made 'em out of plain cement and Texas sand. Naturally, you know where they got the sand? Right out of the hollow tooth, two or three yards of it, all blowed in during the storm.

HOT TIMES

YOU MEAN TO STAND THERE and tell me it's too hot to weed the potatoes? Let me tell you children somethin'—it ain't too hot for the pigweed to grow up and choke them 'tatoes to death, so don't come in here with big eyes askin' for stories when they's vital work to be done. Why, it ain't nearly so hot around here as it was sometimes when I was a boy. Those days was *really* hot.

I remember one summer in particular. Sun was so hot you couldn't leave your ax out in the open, 'cause the heat would just take the temper right out of the steel. Got so bad around midday the fence posts would bend over in the middle, and a log layin' in the field would crawl off into the shade somewhere to cool off. There was a dog chasin' a cat right through the barnyard there, and it was so hot they was both just walkin'. Heat came right down the stovepipe from outside, and we had to throw water on the stove to keep it cool enough to cook on. When we pumped at the well, nothin' but steam came out; we had to catch the steam and let it set overnight to turn back to water.

Folks didn't pasteurize milk those days, but wasn't any need to, 'cause the milk came out of the cows already pasteurized. That heat sure was hard on the corn too. Corn just popped right off the ears till it looked like the ground was covered with snow. It was too hot even for the creek; 'bout ten in the mornin' the water in the creek just stopped still and wouldn't get movin' again till 'bout six in the evenin'.

Even the railroad tracks couldn't take it. Just after cock crow in the mornin', the tracks burrowed under the ground and stayed there till night. Had to change the whole Southern Pacific time-table 'count of that. So don't tell me it's too hot today to weed the 'tato patch, 'cause this hot is just plain cool to me. Somebody go get me my coat.

THE CHAMPION

LIKE I TOLD YOU BEFORE, humanfolks are pretty much like other critters when it come to thinkin' up tricks to outsmart one another. And it wasn't no different in the old days either. You can figure there's always someone ready to outdo somebody else. A stick can beat a dog, but a fire can burn the stick, and water can put out the fire, and a hog can drink up the water, and a man can eat the hog—that's what I mean. A man can be real stout, but once he comes up against another stout man, he got to start *thinkin'*, 'cause he needs more than strength on his side. It's like one of those champion fighters they had on the plantations in slave times.

'Mongst all them slaves was some pretty powerful men who could outwrestle and outfight all the others. Up the river from here there was a master named Colonel Seabrook. He'd just bought him five hundred new slaves, and one of 'em was a fellow named Big John—about the biggest and stoutest man the Colonel ever saw. This man Big John got to be champion of the whole plantation in no time at all. Wouldn't no one fool around with him.

Colonel Seabrook he's talkin' one day with the master of the next plantation up the river, name of Colonel Green. Well,

Colonel Seabrook tell Colonel Green like this: "I got the biggest, stoutest, toughest old champion on the river at my place. Reckon he can beat anyone in a fight."

Colonel Green he say, "I don't know about that. Maybe he's stout, but he ain't so stout as one I got on my place."

"What's the name of the champion on your place?" Colonel Seabrook ask him.

"My champion's named Juke," Colonel Green say, "and he can whup anything on the river, includin' panthers and wildcats."

"Well, I'll tell you," Colonel Seabrook say, "I'll bet you the one I got can whup the one you got."

"Ain't no one can whup my champion," Colonel Green say.

"I'll bet you one thousand dollars," Colonel Seabrook say, "that my Big John can whup your Juke, or else scare him so bad he won't fight."

"I'll bet you," Colonel Green say, "but I hate to take your money so easy."

"Where these men goin' to fight?" Colonel Seabrook say.

"On your place," Colonel Green say, "next Saturday. You get all your folks together there, and I'll be along with Juke at ten o'clock."

Colonel Seabrook he went home then and told Big John he just got him a big fight for next Saturday, for a thousand-dollar bet.

Big John he say, "Colonel, who'm I goin' to fight?"

"You goin' to fight Colonel Green's champion, named Juke."

That gave Big John somethin' to think on, and he tell Old Master: "Colonel, I don't believe I can whup Colonel Green's champion, but maybe I can scare him so bad he'll refuse to fight. Just let me know where the fight goin' to be."

"Right over yonder," Colonel Seabrook say. Big John look at the place and fix it in his mind.

Day before the fight, Big John went down to the woods and dug up a big water oak by the roots. And he took a mule and dragged that tree up to the place where the fight was goin' to be. He dug him a hole and set the water oak up in it and packed the dirt around. When he finished he put leaves around, and it looked just like that tree had growed up on that spot. He took his wife's washtub and clothes and things and put 'em under the tree to make it look natural.

On Saturday mornin' Big John tied himself around the middle with a long grass line, with a weak spot in the middle. And when they saw Colonel Green comin' up to the place with Juke and a crowd of other folks from his plantation, Colonel Seabrook led Big John out to the water oak and tied him to it. Colonel Green come up and say, "Is that your champion who's goin' to fight my champion?"

Colonel Seabrook say, "Yeah, that's him all right."

Colonel Green say, "Why you got him tied up that way?"

"Got to keep him tied," Colonel Seabrook say, "he got an ambitious streak in him. 'Fraid that when he see your champion, he'll bust loose from me and go after him. He's got a bad temper when he gets worked up. Got to tie him up like this sometimes to keep him from tearin' everything to pieces. Have to keep him under control till the fight starts, so's I can talk to him."

When Juke see Big John tied up to the tree that way, he say to his master. "You mean I'm goin' to fight a man they got to tie up to a tree?"

Just then Colonel Seabrook say, "You want me to try him on that rope once to see how strong he is?"

Colonel Green say, "Yeah, I like to see that."

"John," Colonel Seabrook say, "pull on that rope once for the Colonel."

Big John, he leaned against the rope and pulled. The tree bent and started to come up at the roots. When Colonel Green's field hands saw that, they begin to back up.

Juke he said, "Death ain't but death, so why don't you take your gun and shoot me down? I'd rather do that than fight a man who pulls out a water oak by the roots."

Colonel Seabrook say, "Want to see him pull again?"

Juke he call out to his master, "Shoot me down first!"

Then Big John braced his feet and pulled again. The water oak bent some more, and the roots started snappin' out of the ground like popcorn. 'Bout that time all Colonel Green's slaves was backin' up fast, and Juke just stood there shakin'. "Death ain't but death," Juke say, "so shoot me down before I got to fight a man like him!"

Big John set his feet to pull again. Colonel Seabrook holler, "Wait, don't do that!"

But Big John pulled some more, and the water oak started down.

"Don't let 'im pull no more!" Colonel Green hollered. "He's goin' to frighten my champion to death, and I'm gettin' scared too!"

Colonel Seabrook he talkin' to Big John tellin' him not to pull no more. But Big John pullin' and hollerin' back, "Let me at 'im! Let me at the whole bunch!" He give one more good pull and the tree begin to fall, and just then the grass line broke at the weak spot, and Big John came a-runnin'.

When Juke see that, he lit out like a jack rabbit 'cross the plowed ground, with all Colonel Green's other slaves after him. They just sold out, runnin' every-which-way through the corn and cotton. Colonel Green he counted out one thousand dollars and paid it to Colonel Seabrook, 'count of his champion was scared to fight Big John.

Big John he was just as scared as Juke, but his wits saved him.

THE SKULL

ONE OF THE BIG THINGS lots of folks never seem to learn is when to quit talkin'. Some got sense enough to tell only a little bit of what they know, maybe only half, but there's others just can't stop once they get started. Back in the old days there was a slave who didn't know that you got to keep part of what you learn to yourself.

He was out in the woods cuttin' posts one day with the other slaves, and on the way home he lagged behind. Whilst walkin', he was a-kickin' around in the grass with his feet. And whilst doin' that, he kicked somethin' that rolled out in the open. You know what it was? A white, dry skull, been layin' there a long time. Well, this slave was sorry to kick a skull like that, and he say, " 'Scuse me, skull, let me put you back where you come from."

But 'fore he could pick it up, he heard music, and he looked around, not seein' no one. 'Twas a voice, singin' a language he didn't understand a bit of, except only two-three words:

"Aga chaymo, bahga momo, fray kolee,
Do what I done, then you'll see."

Then he see it was the skull on the ground was singin' those words. When the skull quiet down for a time, he say to it, "Man, how come you here?"

The skull say to him, "My big mouth done this to me."

That slave he couldn't wait to get home and tell what he saw. He found Old Master and told him he was just makin' conversation with a talkin' skull in the woods.

Old Master he don't like to hear wild stories like that, he say he goin' to put a stop to it. So he gone out to the woods with this slave, and the slave found the skull, and all the other folks stood around waitin' for the skull to talk. The slave he say, "Boy, tell Old Master what you told me!" But the skull don't make a sound. Slave say, "Man, sing that song once more!" But nary a sound come out of that skull at all.

Old Master he say to this slave, "I knows you been drinkin' and I goin' to put a stop to it. Got to give you a good thrashin'."

So he gave that slave a good whuppin' and left him in the woods to sober up. After everyone gone, you know what? That skull sang his little song again:

"Aga chaymo, bahga momo, fray kolee,
Do what I done, then you'll see."

The slave sat up and looked mournful at the skull, sayin', "Brother, what took you so long?"

Skull said, "My big mouth done this to me, son. Your big mouth done this to you too."

OLD MASTER AND OKRA

OLD MASTER—he owned the big plantation in slavery times—
Old Master had to go down to New Orleans on business, and he
left his number-one slave named Okra in charge of things. Okra
declared to himself he goin' to have a good time whilst Old Master
was away, and the thing he did the very first mornin' was to go
out and tell the other slaves, "Now you get on with your affairs.
Old Master gone to New Orleans and we got to keep things goin'."

Then Okra went in the kitchen to cook himself up some food,
and in the process of doin' so he got ruffled and spilled the bacon
grease on top of the stove. It burst up into a big fire, and next thing
you know that house was goin' up in flame and smoke. Okra he
went out the window and stood off a ways, lookin' real sorry. By
the time the other hands got there, wasn't nothin' else to do *but*
look sorry. They was so busy with lookin' that they never noticed
that the sparks lit in the wood lot and set it afire too. Well, Okra
ordered everybody out to the wood lot to save it, but by then the
grass was sizzlin' and poppin', a regular old prairie fire roarin'
across the fields, burnin' up the cotton and everything else. They
run over there with wet bags to beat it out, but next thing they
knowed, the pasture was afire and all Old Master's cattle was
a-goin', throttle out and racin' for the Texas Badlands.

Okra went to the barn for the horses, but soon's he opened the door they bolted and was gone. "If'n I can get that ox team hitched," Okra said, "I'll go on down to Colonel Thatcher's place and get some help." Well, minute he started to put the yoke on them oxen, the left-hand ox lit out and was gone. The right-hand ox went after him, and the both of 'em just left Okra holdin' the ox yoke up in the air. When Old Master's huntin' dog see them oxen go off that way, he figured something was wrong, and he sold out, barkin' and snappin' at their heels.

'Bout that time Okra looked around and found all the slaves had took off, too, headin' North and leavin' no tracks. He was all alone, and he had to digest all that misery by himself.

Week or two went by, and Okra went down to meet the boat Old Master comin' back on. Old Master got off feelin' pretty good. Told Okra to carry his stuff and say, "Well, Okra, how'd things go while I was away?"

"Fine, just fine," Okra say. "I notice they're fixin' the bridge over Black Creek. Ain't that good?"

"Yeah," Old Master say, "that's fine, Okra, just fine. Soon's we get home I'm goin' to change my clothes and do some quail shootin'."

"Captain," Okra say, hangin' his head, "I got a little bad news for you."

"What's that?" Old Master say.

"You ain't neither goin' quail huntin'," Okra say, "your huntin' dog run away."

Old Master took it pretty good. He say, "Well, don't worry about it none, he'll come back. How'd he happen to run away?"

"Chasin' after the right-hand ox," Okra say. "That ox just lit out one mornin'."

"Where to?" Old Master say.

"I don't know where to," Okra say. "He was tryin' to catch up with the left-hand ox."

Old Master began to frown now, and he say to Okra, "You mean the whole ox team is gone? How come?"

"I was yokin' 'em up to go after Colonel Thatcher, after the horses bolted," Okra say.

"How come the horses bolted?" Old Boss say.

"Smoke from the pasture grass. That's what scared all your livestock and made 'em break down the fence and run for the swamp."

"You mean all my livestock is gone? Okra, I goin' to skin you. How'd that pasture get on fire?"

Okra he just stood there lookin' foolish, scratchin' his head. "Reckon the fire just came across from the cotton field, Captain," he say.

"You mean my cotton's burned!" Old Master holler. "How'd that happen?"

"Couldn't put it out, Captain. Soon as we see it come over there from the wood lot, we went down with wet bags but we couldn't handle it. Man, that was sure a pretty cotton field before the fire got there."

Right now Old Master was lookin' pretty sick. He talk kind of weak. "Okra, you tryin' to tell me the wood lot's gone too?"

"I hate to tell you, Captain, but you guessed it," Okra say, kind of sad. "Imagine, all them trees gone, just 'cause of one lonesome spark."

Old Master couldn't hardly talk at all now. He just whisperin'. "Okra," he say, "Okra, where'd that spark come from?"

"Wind blew it right from the house," Okra say, "it was when the big timbers gave and came down. Man, sparks flew in the air a mile or more."

"You mean the house burned up?" Old Master say.

"Oh, yeah, didn't I tell you?" Okra reply. "Didn't burn *up*, though, so much as it burned *down*."

By now Old Master was a miserable sight, pale as a ghost and shakin' all over.

"Okra, Okra," Old Master say, "let's go get the field hands together and do somethin'!"

"Can't do that," Okra say, "I forget to tell you, they's all sold out for Michigan."

Old Master just set there shakin' his head back and forth. "Okra," he say, "why didn't you come right out with it? Why you tell me everything was fine?"

"Captain, I'm sorry if I didn't tell it right," Okra say. "Just wanted to break it to you easy."

THE DO-ALL AX

NO, DON'T KNOW as I can tell you anything with magic in it.
How you expect I can tell you about magic when they ain't no
such thing? Of course, there's two-three exceptions, like those
flyin' slaves in the old days. Folks say there was a couple of field
hands down around Johnson's Landing who didn't like the way
they was bein' treated as slaves, and they just flapped their arms
and took off. When last seen they was over the water headed east
like a ball of fire.

Then there was that do-all ax. It sure got magic in it, what I
mean.

The way it was, in the old days there was a man who had this
do-all ax. When it was time to clear the trees off the ground to do
some plantin', this man'd take his ax and his rockin' chair and go
out and sit down in the shade. Then he'd sing a kind of song:

> "Bo kee meeny, dah ko dee,
> Field need plantin', get off my knee."

That ax would just jump off his knee and start choppin'
wood without no one holdin' onto the handle or anything. All by

itself it went around cuttin' down the timber till the field was cleared. Then it chopped up the trees into stovewood lengths and threw 'em in a pile in the barnyard.

And next thing you know, this ax turn itself into a plow and went to plowin' up the field to make ready for plantin'. And when that's done, the plow turn into a corn planter and plant the corn.

All the time this man who owned it was rockin' back and forth in the shade, fannin' himself with a leaf. Well, that corn was sure-enough magic corn, grew up almost as fast as it went in the ground; little sprouts start to pop out 'fore the sun went down.

'Bout this time the man sing another song:

"Kah bo denny, brukko bay,
Time for dinner, quit this play."

Then the corn planter turned itself back into an ax and stopped workin'.

Well, three-four days later that corn was tall and ready for hoein'. Man went out with his ax, and it turned into a hoe. It went up and down the rows by itself, hoein' corn till the whole field was done. Next week the man came back and the hoe turn itself into a corn knife to cut all them stalks down. You see, the whole job was done just by this here magic ax.

Other folks used to come around and watch all these goin's-on. Everybody figure if they only had an ax like that, life would be a powerful lot better for them.

There was one man named Kwako who wanted that ax more'n anyone else. Said he reckoned he'd about die if he didn't get that ax. And when there wasn't nobody home one time, this Kwako went in and took it. Figured he'd get his own work done and then bring the ax back and wouldn't nobody know the difference.

He ran home and got his own rockin' chair and went out in the field. Laid the ax across his lap and sang like the other man did:

> "Bo kee meeny, dah ko dee,
> Field need plantin', get off my knee."

Man, that ax went to work. Chopped down all the trees, cut the wood up in stovewood lengths, and stacked it by the house. Then it turned itself to a plow and plowed the ground. Then it turned to a corn planter and planted corn. 'Bout the time it was done plantin', the corn sprouts was already pokin' through the ground.

Kwako he was mighty pleased when he see all that. He sat rockin' back and forth in the shade enjoyin' himself real good. So when the corn was all planted he hollered, "That's enough for now, come on home." But corn planter didn't pay no attention, just kept jumpin' all around. Kwako hollered, "Didn't you hear what I said? Quit all this foolishness and come on home." Trouble was, he didn't know the song to stop it. He should have said:

> "Kah bo denny, brukko bay,
> Time for dinner, quit this play."

But he didn't know the words, and he just kept hollerin', and the corn planter just kept jumpin' around, plantin' corn every-which-way till the seed was all gone. Then it turned into a hoe and started hoein' up the field. Now, that corn wasn't tall enough to be hoed, and it got all chopped to little pieces. Man, that field was a mess. Kwako he ran back and forth tryin' to catch the hoe, but he couldn't make it, hoe moved around too fast. Next thing you know, the hoe turned into a corn knife and started cuttin' in the air. But wasn't no corn to cut. So it went over in the cotton field and started cuttin' down the cotton. Just laid that cotton field low. And then it moved west, cuttin' down everything in the way. And when last seen it was followin' the settin' sun. After that it was gone for good.

Since that time there hasn't ever been a magic do-all ax in this part of the world, and folks has to do their farmin' the hard way.

But get it out of your head that there's magic things round-about. What I told you is true, but it's an *exception*.

THE KING AND KUFFIE

YOU KNOWS ALL ABOUT COOKIN', girl, don't you? Now, what's the best and most important thing we got to eat? We got cows, hogs, chickens, and guineas outside, not to mention corn and greens in the garden, and rice and lard in the cupboard. Which one of 'em is the most important?

The way it was, there was a king who was lookin' for a man to take charge of a lot of important affairs for him. Kings like to eat, you know, and they always gettin' special dishes cooked up for 'em. Well, this particular king had his eye on a man named Kuffie that he thought would make a pretty good helper, and he figure to try him out to see how smart he is. He call Kuffie up to his office and say, "Kuffie, Thursday is cook's night out, and I wonder can you cook me something for dinner?"

Kuffie say sure, he could do that, all right.

King say, "Kuffie, what I want from you isn't just ordinary rice and greens and stuff. I want you to fix me the best and most important dish in the whole world. You reckon you can do that?"

Kuffie say sure, he can do it.

When Thursday come, King told Kuffie to come on with the food. Kuffie brought it out. King sniffed at it. He say, "Kuffie, it sure smells good. What is it?"

84

"Cow tongue," Kuffie say. "Regular old cow tongue."

"I always liked cow tongue," King say, "but what I want to know is how come it's the most important thing there is?"

"Well, King," Kuffie say, "it's like this. You got a mighty important job and for folks like that there ain't nothin' more important than tongue. That is, if it's used rightly. With a tongue you can tell folks what to do right and also what they doin' wrong. When they's trouble in the community you can go amongst the folks and calm everyone down. A tongue give the preacher power to preach the Gospel. That's mighty important, ain't it? Yeah, and when you havin' trouble with the king in the next country, a tongue give him your side of the argument. When a man been done wrong, a tongue give him the chance to tell about it and get justice, don't it?

"You got some cotton to sell and somebody want to buy it, they asks you how much you want for it, and you say so much a bale. It's tongues that make all that possible, now, isn't it? Without no tongues it'd be mighty difficult to do things. And take a cryin' baby. Who goin' to sing that baby to sleep if they ain't got tongues? If my wife didn't have no tongue, how she goin' to call me for dinner?

"Now, King, it's even more important with you," Kuffie say. "You got lots of work to tell people to do. Without no tongue how you goin' to tell the boys to get out and plant cotton or fix the roads or patch the roof or anything else? And how you goin' to shout in church if you got no tongue? That's why tongue is the best and most important thing there is for a King."

Well, King just sat there and took it all in. When Kuffie got through, King say, "Kuffie, you sold me. I never see it before, but I see it now. But before I make anybody my assistant I got to know for sure what they got on the ball. I want you to fix me somethin' to eat again next Thursday, same time. I'll be here. Want somethin' different next time though, Kuffie. Next time I want you to make me the worst thing to have in the whole world. Not the most good, but the worst. You reckon you can do that?"

"Naturally I can do it," Kuffie tell the King. "Any kind of cookin' you want, I can do it."

"All right then, and don't be late," King say.

Next Thursday on cook's day off, King holler for Kuffie to come on with the food, he's ready. Kuffie brought on a big plate of stuff, all boiled up with greens and things.

"Here it is," he say, "just what you ask for."

King look at it and smell some of it. "Man," he say, "it sure smells bad. What is it?"

"Cow tongue," Kuffie say, "just old cow tongue."

"Man," King say to Kuffie, "last time you tell me tongue is the best thing there is. What happen?"

"The only difference is what you can do with it," Kuffie say. "Tongue can be the *worst* kind of thing. Take folks which is gettin' along fine and then somebody start some gossip with his tongue. Next thing you know everybody sayin' things that ain't so about some folks and ruin their reputation. Everybody is peaceable and friendly, and then somebody gets to talkin' about things and stirrin' up trouble. Next thing you know, half the folks has turned against the other half, and nobody don't listen to reason.

"Take a king, he's talkin' to another king and say something that make the other king mad, and after that they have a big war and lots of innocent folks get killed. Ain't that bad? It's tongue that does it. Look what liars and hypocrites do with their tongues. You see what I mean?"

The King took it all in, what Kuffie was sayin'. "Kuffie," he say, "you sure told me. This here dish stinks pretty bad, you better take it out. You come on back here next week and be my helper. You'll get fifty dollars a week, and start Monday eight o'clock."

And that's how come Kuffie got where he did.

OLD BOSS, JOHN, AND THE MULE

How you like to hear somethin' about Old Boss? You know Old Boss, all right. He's the man had that big cotton plantation down the river.

Well, one time Old Boss had a man workin' for him named John. If they was anything this John liked best, it was sleepin'. He'd be up at cock crow, all right, chop up a stack of stove wood, and get started out to the field.

First he'd hook up Old Boss' mule, talkin' sweet-like, "We goin' to plow a good stretch for Old Boss today, ain't we, Jim?" All that was just in case Old Boss might be watchin'. But when John got out there on the new ground he'd plow three-four furrows and then head for the big maple tree in the far corner. He'd tie the mule up and lay down in the shade and go to sleep. Every day it was like that. John couldn't wait to get up in the morning so's he could go out there and get some sleep.

After two-three days Old Boss say, "Ain't you got that field plowed yet, John?"

And John say, "Boss, that mule is the laziest, orneriest mule I ever work with."

Old Boss say, "John, you got to *encourage* him. Use the stick a little every once in a while."

Well, after that, when it was time to come home, John'd drive the mule up on the hill and whack him with a stick four-five times, hollerin', "Git movin', you lazy, good-for-nothin' mule! You give me a mess of trouble today! When I say walk, *walk!*" Then he'd come in and take the harness off and get ready to eat.

But next mornin', naturally, he'd head for that big maple tree and do some more sleepin'.

One day when John was just settlin' down for shut-eye, the mule turned his head around and talked to him. He say, "Reckon it's about time I had a good talk with Old Boss."

Well, that John sat right up straight and looked around. Looked north and south, then up in the air, but he didn't see no one but the mule.

"Who said that?" John say.

"I said it," the mule say, "and I'm goin' to do it too."

John he commence to shake so hard he couldn't hardly get up.

"You the first mule I ever hear could talk," John say.

"You ain't heard no talkin' yet to speak of," the mule say. "I got a thing or two to put in Old Boss' ear."

"What you goin' to talk about?" John say.

"Plenty, that's what, plenty," the mule say. "Goin' to mention how you get out here every mornin' and go to sleep in the shade, 'stead of workin'. Then on the way home you take me up on the hill and whup me with that stick, like I give you trouble all day. I'm goin' to give Old Boss somethin' to think on."

When John hear that, he got up and sold out, headed for home. Old Boss see him burnin' up the ground comin' in to the barn.

"What's up John?" Old Boss say.

"Old Boss," John say, "I quit. I ain't goin' to drive no mule that talks. And besides that, if that mule tell you somethin' about me, it's a big lie."

John he went in the barn and sat down. Ain't nothin' Old Boss could say to make him go back after the mule. After a while he went himself, with his yellow dog runnin' along after him. Found the mule under the big maple tree, right where John left him.

"Hear you can talk," Old Boss say to the mule, but the mule don't say a thing, just grazin' in the grass.

Old Boss drive the mule home and put him in the barn.

Then he give John a good talkin' to, tellin' him if he don't mend his ways he goin' to have to get a new field hand.

All John would say was, "Boss, I don't fool around with talkin' mules."

"I'm pretty put out with you," Boss say and start on up to the house. Halfway there he shake his head, sayin', "Don't know what I'm goin' to do with that boy. Sure don't know."

Right then his yellow dog speak up, sayin', "Fire him, Boss. You got no choice."

"What's that?" Boss say, lookin' at the dog.

"Sure, fire him," the dog say. "When a man start to imagine things like that boy does, 'bout time to get rid of him."

Well, now, which one you think is the fool, John or Old Boss? 'Course, it don't say if Old Boss fired him or not. But if Old Boss is hearin' animals talk too, it don't hardly put him in a better position than John, do it?

CROSSING THE RIVER

ONE TIME Old Boss sent John to town to do some business for him there. John set off and came to the river ford right after a heavy rain. Looked to him like the water had come up pretty high since he been there before. He stood on the bank studyin' about it, wonderin' could he make it across.

"Last time I crossed here it came up to my ankles," John say. "I wonder how deep is it now?"

Just then a big old bullfrog come up on the bank and settled down. When he got his wind good, he gave out a croak or two, like this: "Knee deep! Knee deep! Knee deep!" John perked up his ears at that, sayin', "Frog, you know what you talkin' about?"

Frog he just set there croakin', "Knee deep! Knee deep! Knee deep!"

John he say, "Man, if you don't know how deep this water is, who does?" And right then and there he took off his shoes and started to wade across. When he got to the middle the water was over his head and he had to swim for it. And all the time Buh Bullfrog just set there croakin', "Knee deep! Knee deep! Knee deep!" just like that.

It was the first time John found out that when a bullfrog say, "knee deep" he's just pleasurin' himself with the sound of his voice and don't mean a thing by it. This is the kind of talk you got to watch out for, when people just pleasurin' themselves with the sound of their own voice. It sure can make a pile of trouble.

OLD BOSS AND GEORGE

I GOT ANOTHER ONE to tell you about Old Boss and a different field hand, named George. Don't recall if George was before John or after John, Old Boss had so many.

George he had different habits, though. He could *work*, what I mean. He made Old Boss' mule really *walk*, practically wore him out. George was six-feet-four, wore number-twelve shoes. Come cotton-pickin' time, George picked eight-nine hundred pounds of cotton without half tryin'. When he was *tryin'*, well, man, you never saw nothin' like it. Cotton bolls moved through the air so fast folks thought it was snowin'. If they was fence posts to be dug, this George dug 'em. If they was hoein' to be done, he hoed. Folks from all over used to tell Old Boss what a good worker this George was. Old Boss was proud about it too.

Soon one mornin' rain started to come down, and Old Boss figured there wouldn't be no field work done that day. So he called George out to the barn where he had six or seven sacks of potato seed. "George," he said, "might as well cut 'tato seed today. Leave the poor 'tatoes be. Put 'em in a pile over there. Pick out the good 'tatoes for seed and cut 'em in quarters. Put 'em right here in this tub."

Old Boss went back in the house and didn't hear no more from George. Two or three o'clock in the afternoon he say, "I sure forgot about George. He's out there in that barn still cuttin' seed 'tatoes."

When Old Boss get back to the barn, there was George settin' on the crate where he left him, right in front of the tub with a 'tato in one hand and a knife in the other. Old Boss looked in the tub. Saw five or six pieces of 'tato, that's all.

"George," Old Boss say, "you been cuttin' 'tato seed all mornin'?"

"Yeah," George say.

"Where they at?" Old Boss say.

"In the tub," George say.

"You mean that's all you done, George?" Old Boss ask him. George he just hang his head.

"I'm sure disappointed," Old Boss say. "All the folks 'round here knows you're a steady worker. You can pick more cotton than just about anybody on the river. You can dig post holes like nobody's business. You're mighty stout with an ax in your hand too. You milk faster'n anybody I ever had 'round here. You walk that mule crazy with plowin'. How come you only got six bits of 'tato in that tub, George?"

Well, that George he just hang his head for true this time, hearin' Old Boss talk that way.

"Old Boss," he say, "I'm a real sorry man. I sure don't mind plowin' or cuttin' trees or pickin' cotton or mostly anything else. But there's one thing about it, this trying to make up my mind is too much for me."

DEVIL IN CHURCH

O F ALL THE PLACES you expect you might meet up with the Devil, you never figure to see him in church, now, do you? But the Devil have a lot of experience, and he say you got to fight fire with fire, water with water, and wind with wind. He don't *have* to hang around places like Sodom and Gomorrah, 'cause he ain't needed there. Folks in those places already doin' his bad work for him. 'Nother thing, the Devil can't always go around *lookin'* like the Devil. If he did that, he ain't goin' to get nowhere. He got to pass himself off like ordinary people. Sometimes he even got to pray and shout like he been saved. Now there ain't nothin' more against the Devil's nature than that, is there? I'll tell you what I mean.

Well, one day the Devil looked around and say, "Sure is quiet around here. Ain't nothin' bad happenin' today. Guess I'll make some trouble."

So he picked out one small half-sized Devil and tell him, "Boy, you go on up there and corrupt some folks today, make 'em mean and sinful. Get goin' now."

This Little Devil, he got dressed up, tucked his tail in good, and went up to find some folks to make 'em sinful. He got to

95

town just about church time on Sunday. When he saw all the folks goin' into church, he say, "Looks to me like I got to go in there after those people."

So he went into church and sat down in the back row, waitin' till the service was over. Preacher preached, people moaned and shouted, and the Little Devil just sat and waited. When service was over, the Little Devil got busy runnin' around tryin' to corrupt folks by tellin' them to do bad things. But they didn't pay him no mind. sayin', "Don't believe we ever see you around here before.

Brother." Well, the Little Devil got mighty discouraged after a while and went home.

"You corrupt a lot of good folks up there?" the Big Devil ask him.

"Uh-uh," the Little Devil say.

"Well," the Big Devil say, kind of mad, "what you spend all your time at?"

"I went up just like you told me," the Little Devil say. "All the folks were goin' to church, so I went in and sat in the back row till they got through. And then wouldn't no one talk to me after that."

Big Devil he just shook his head, lookin' kind of sad at the Little Devil, like he was pretty stupid. "Man," he say, "don't you know that if you goin' to get along, you got to fight fire with fire, water with water, iron with iron, and air with air? You got to do what the *other* folks do. If you goin' to church to do your work, you can't sit in the back row. You got to get up on the mourner's bench and shout and moan and groan with the rest of them. If you'd done that, wouldn't nobody have said they hadn't never seen you before. If you playin' baseball with the folks, you got to hit a home run to win their respect. If you doin' it with music, you got to make 'em dance. And if you doin' it in church, you really got to get sanctified. Man, you sure got a lot to learn."

PREACHER AND THE DEVIL

IF YOU GOIN' to stand there and allow as you saw a bear sittin' on Uncle Jim's porch readin' a newspaper, that calls for some close examination. Could be you got yourself *influenced* into thinkin' you saw it. Could be there was a real bear there too, but 'tain't likely. I see plenty of bears in my time, and ain't none of 'em learned their letters. The way people are, they're always tryin' to see something other folks ain't seen, and that's a powerful influence on the imagination. And if they gets a little boost from the Devil, ain't no tellin' what they goin' to come up with.

Like the time the Devil was moseyin' around tryin' to figure out some devilment to do. He done so many devilments in his time he couldn't hardly think of no new ones. Then he see the preacher comin' along the road, and he say to himself, "Man, I got a good one to do on the preacher. I'm goin' to get him to tell about the biggest lie folks around here ever heard."

So he tucked his tail inside his clothes good and act mighty sweet. When the preacher come along he say, "Mornin', Reverend, mighty fine mornin'."

"Yeah, Brother, it sure is," Preacher say. "You a stranger 'round here?"

"Just passin' through," the Devil say, "reckon I'll be around till Monday or Tuesday."

"Well, ain't that nice," Preacher say. "You'll be right welcome at church tomorrow."

"That's sure nice of you," Devil say. "What you goin' to preach on?"

"Brother," Preacher say, "David and Goliath is my text for tomorrow."

"That sounds fine to me," Devil say. "How big you 'spects that Goliath was?"

"Well, Brother, he was sure bigger'n you or me. I reckon he might have stood about nine feet tall."

Devil shook his head. "Well, that's a disappointment to me. You know things was a lot bigger in them old days. Everything was different. Take Methuselah, now didn't he live nine hundred years? If you say a man around here live to one hundred, that's pretty old; but if you talkin' about Methuselah, one hundred years ain't nothin'. If you tell folks that Goliath was only nine feet tall, they ain't goin' to be impressed. If you want to get that congregation of yours rockin' and reelin', you got to make things real big, what I mean."

Devil he went on talkin' this way, Preacher listenin' and takin' it all in.

"I tell you what," Preacher say, "you goin' to be there tomorrow, you just set in the front row and give me the nod. If you think somethin' got to be a little bigger, bob your head up and down, and I'll be much obliged."

"Fine," the Devil say, "I'll set right in the front row."

Next mornin' was Sunday and when the preacher get up there to preach, he see this stranger sittin' right in the front row showin' all his teeth.

Preacher open up his Bible, slap his hand on the table, and begin.

"This mornin' we goin' to talk about David the shepherd boy," Preacher say, "right from the First Book of Samuel. This boy David was the son of Jesse, and he was pretty sharp. And the Philistines was comin' down on the Israelites, and they had a champion fighter 'mongst 'em name Goliath. Now, 'cordin' to the Good Book, the Philistines sent their champion out to the field to challenge the stoutest man 'mongst the Israelites to a fight. And he stood up there in the middle of the field and wasn't no Israelite wanted to fight him, 'cause Goliath was six cubits tall, and that make nine feet from head to toe."

Preacher he looked down in the first row to see what this stranger thinks, and he see the Devil bobbin' his head up and down. So the preacher think he can do a little better by Goliath, and he say: "Come to think of it, that nine feet was afore he was altogether full growed. He was eight cubits tall, and that make about twelve feet top to bottom." Preacher see the Devil still bobbin' his head. "But that was before he stretched himself out to his full height," Preacher tell the congregation. "You might say he was closer to fifteen or *twenty* feet altogether. Fact is, I'm pretty sure he was about as high as the steeple on the Presbyterian Church, and that was only when he was a little bit hunched down." Devil stopped bobbin' his head and showed his teeth, so Preacher relaxed a bit.

"Yes, Brothers and Sisters, and this man had a spear that weighed more'n fifty pounds, and the shaft was sixty feet long." Preacher looked down and see the Devil pushin' out his lips and shakin' his head up and down like he was mighty put out. So Preacher say: "But that's only 'cordin' to one way of lookin' at the matter. Another way of lookin' at it, that spear weighed around four hundred pounds and was as big around the shaft as that old elm tree out in front.

"Well, then, David the shepherd boy come out across the field with his slingshot and picked up a stone about as big as a buckshot . . ." Preacher see the Devil bobbin' his head like it was about to fall off. "Well, then, about as big as a watermelon," he say. Devil's head was still bobbin'. "Come to think of it, that stone was about as big as a bale of cotton, and if you figure the size of it, and made of stone all the way through, it must have weighed more'n a thousand pounds.

"And David the shepherd boy, only 'bout five feet four tall—or maybe only four foot five . . . or I guess you could say he was only about half that size—hit Goliath in the head with that stone from his slingshot and killed him dead. And when Goliath fell he was so tall he stretched out on the ground from Shochoh to Azekah."

Preacher looked sideways, and see the Devil bobbin' his head somethin' awful, so he say: "Old Goliath he stretched, you might say, from Shochoh to Jerusalem." Devil sat there still a-bobbin' away. "You might say Goliath stretched all the way from Shochoh to Mobile," Preacher say. "And if we don't adjourn this meetin' right now we goin' to have him layin' *right on top of us.*"

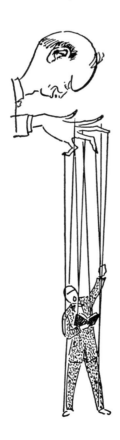

WHAT THE PREACHER'S TALKING ABOUT

Now if a preacher can talk a lot, he can also talk a *little,* and I got in mind a particular preacher who come to church one Sunday mornin' and got up in the pulpit to preach. After the openin' prayer he stand up there, put on his specs, and open the book in front of him.

"Brothers and Sisters," he say, "good mornin' to you all. It's a sunshiny world this mornin', and I likes the look of all those happy faces sittin' out there in front of me. Now I wonder if all you folks know what I'm goin' to preach to you about this day?"

Well, folks in church is always ready to answer the preacher, and they all call out, "No, Reverend, we don't know what you goin' to preach about."

When the preacher heard that, he took off his specs and look around the church, shakin' his head like he's mighty disappointed. He say, "Well, what use is it for me to preach to you, and you don't know what I'm talkin' about?" And he snap his book shut and went off the pulpit and went home.

Next Sunday the folks went to church early and stood around figurin' what to do. Lots of 'em come a long way to hear some preachin' and they don't want to be done out of it. After a while they got it all studied out what they goin' to tell the preacher that mornin'.

He gets up on the pulpit, lookin' in his book while the folks singin' the openin' prayer, then he stand up.

"Mornin' to you all, Brothers and Sisters, and a fine day it is. Now I ask you, do you know what I'm talkin' about this mornin'?"

That whole congregation holler back, "Yes, Reverend, we know."

When the preacher hear this, he snap his book shut and say: " 'Pears to me that if you all know what I'm talkin' about, ain't no use of my sayin' a word."

And he went right off the pulpit, got in his carriage, and went home.

After that the congregation did some real serious studyin' about the situation. Looked like the preacher had 'em comin' and goin'. But next Sunday, when the service commenced, they was ready.

Preacher looked all around the church, from front to back and side to side. Then he put on his specs and say, "Mornin', Brothers and Sisters. Reckon you had somethin' to think on since I saw you last. Now I like to ask you, do you know what I'm talkin' about this mornin'?"

What happen then was one half the congregation rise up and say, "No, Reverend, we don't know what you preachin' 'bout this mornin'." And they sit down and the other half get up and say, "Yes, Reverend, we knows what you talkin' 'bout this mornin'."

Right then the preacher snapped his book closed and took off his specs again. "Seems to me," he say, "that half of you knows and half don't know. So if the half that knows will tell the half that don't know, it'll save me a powerful lot of time. So long."

SHARING THE CROPS

T HE WAY IT WAS, there was a big plantation down the river a ways, and a man went to the owner and say he want to rent a piece of it on shares. Plantation owner, he say, sure, he willin' to rent twenty acres on shares. He go out and show the man the land he got to rent. Everything all set then, but the man gets to talkin' to other croppers in the neighborhood.

"Boy," they say, "you made a sad bargain. That captain you rent your land from goin' to starve you to death."

Naturally, the man got to worryin' about this. All the time he's plowin' up the ground he's studyin' about it. So before he plants anything he goes callin' on the owner, sayin', "Captain, 'scuse me, just one small thing I forgot to ask you. What part of the crop is yours and what part is mine?"

"You got that ground all plowed?" the owner says.

"Yes sir," farmer say, "got it all plowed."

"You got it all harrowed down fine?" the owner ask him.

"Yes, sir, Captain, got it all harrowed," the man say.

"Well, I tell you what," the owner say. "The top half of the crop is mine, and the bottom half is yours."

"Thank you, Captain, thank you, that'll be mighty fine with me," the cropper say, and he go on home.

Now that owner he was a cotton man. Didn't think nothin' but cotton. He figured to get all the value out of the crop and leave the cropper with nothin' at all.

But when the cropper got back to the land, he didn't plant cotton. He planted 'tatoes instead. Couple of months pass by, and the owner come to see how his new cropper doin'. Met him on the road and say, "Man, you ain't forget that agreement we made, 'bout me takin' the top half and you the bottom?"

"No, sir, didn't forget it," the man say.

Just then they come to the field. When the owner see all those 'tatoes and not one boll of cotton, he had a fit.

"When you want me to bring all them 'tato tops over, Captain?" the cropper ask him.

"Keep 'em, keep 'em," the owner say, "you can have my half this year. Next year we goin' to make a different agreement."

Next year 'bout plowin' time the cropper go to see the owner again and say, "Captain, you say you like to make a better arrangement this year. What part of the crop you want?"

"I likes to rotate the arrangement," the owner say, "so this year I'll take the bottom half and you take the top half."

"Yes sir, Captain, that's agreeable to me," the cropper say. He went right home to do his plantin', but he didn't plant no more 'tatoes. He planted oats.

Couple of months went by and the owner come down to see how his crop was doin'.

"Man, you just in time," the cropper say, "come out and look the way everything is growin'."

"Don't forget," the owner say, "this year I get the bottom share and you get the top."

"No, sir, I don't forget it at all," the cropper say.

Right then they come to the field, and the owner sees it's all in oats.

"Where you want the straw delivered?" the cropper ask him. Well, when the owner see he been outsmarted twice, he was plenty mad. "If I let you farm my ground *at all* next year, there's got to be a new arrangement," he say.

"Yes, sir, Captain, you just say the word," the cropper tell him.

"Next year," the owner say, "I'll take the bottom and I'll take the top too."

Cropper scratched his head. "What part that leave for me?" he say.

"The middle part," the owner say, "you can have the middle part."

Next year the cropper plant his field again. 'Round July the owner come down to look things over. Met the cropper on the road again, and they went up to the field together.

"I expect you recollect the nature of our arrangement this year?" he say.

"Oh, yes, Captain. Top and bottom for you, the middle for me."

And when they got out there, you know what the owner find? That whole field been planted in *corn.*

"You got a mighty fine crop of stalks below and tassels above," the cropper say. "But me and my family prefers the ears in the middle. What kind of arrangement you want to make for next year?"

That plantation owner just shake his head.

"Next year won't be no top, bottom, or middle arrangement," he say. "I'll take same as you take, half and half."

And that's the way it was after that. But the first three years gave that cropper a mighty good start in life, and he been doin' fine ever since.

DEATH AND THE OLD MAN

ONCE THERE WAS an old man who was wicked. Just seem like he was always too busy or too lazy to sit down and think about his sins and repent of 'em. Although he was old enough to know better, he never did see fit to think that one day he goin' to die and better get prepared for it.

One day he was on the porch in his rockin' chair and he see a man walkin' up the path to the house. "Evenin'," he say to the man, "you a stranger 'round here?"

"Evenin', Old Man," the stranger say. "No, I ain't no real stranger 'round here. Come through this way every once in a while. My name is Death."

When the old man hear that, he stop rockin'. "Well, evenin', Death," he say. "Didn't expect you. You got business 'round here?"

"Funny how lots of folks don't expect me," Death say. "Yes, I'm on business, Old Man. I come for you. Put on your hat and let's go."

Old Man he didn't want to go. He liked it fine where he was. He say, "Yes, sir, Death, thank you kindly. Mighty fine of you comin' all this way. But I sure could use a little more time. I got a big field of corn out there I got to take care of. Maybe you could drop by again in two-three weeks?"

"Well," Death say, "go tend to your corn, and I'll be back next Saturday." Death went off elsewhere, he had lots of folks to see. So the old man started a-rockin' again in his rockin' chair and smokin' his pipe.

Three-four days went by, and on Saturday mornin' the old man was in the cornfield pullin' weeds. He heard the cornstalks rustlin', and Death was standin' there. "Well, come on, Old Man," Death say, "I'm real busy this mornin' and I can't stand around."

"Good mornin', Death," man say. "It's a fine mornin'. This dew on the ground makes it good for pullin' weeds. How'd you like to give me a hand?"

Death got kind of mad when he hear that. "Now look here, Old Man, I ain't no field hand. I got my own work to do. I got a regular schedule to fill, and I can't be comin' back all the time."

"Death," the man say, "I wonder can you give me a little more time? Folks has a big need for corn, you know, and this field need lots of attention."

"All right, then," Death say, "get on with your weedin'. I'll pick you up next turn around."

"You do that," Old Man say, "just drop in next time you're in the neighborhood." When Death went away, the man went back to weedin' the garden. Fact that Death kept comin' back didn't make no impression on him. He didn't do nothin' to get ready, just went ahead like he always did. Winter went past and the old man forgot all about Death. But he was beginnin' to feel mighty poorly. His rheumatism was gettin' worse. His eyes was gettin' more dim, and he didn't hear so good.

Next spring the old man was in the cornfield again and Death came along. "Come on, Old Man," he say, "it's time now."

"Mornin', Death," Old Man say, "have a chair and rest yourself. How you like some fat pork and corn bread?"

"Now, look here, Old Man," Death say, "I'm real busy and you foolin' me. Put on your hat and come on."

Old Man was studyin' pretty hard about the situation. Didn't want to go along this time any more'n last time.

"Tell you what," he say, "I'm mighty sorry to see you makin' all these trips, and I'm goin' to make it easy for you. You just get on with your work, and next time you figure you need me you can send me a sign and I'll come. Save you a lot of walkin'."

"What kind of sign?" Death ask him.

"A sign I can see or a sign I can hear," Old Man say, "either one. That'll give me a little time to get this corn crop sowed."

"That's a promise, ain't it?" Death say.

"It's a promise," Old Man tell him, "in the name of the Good Book."

"All right then," Death say. "When you hear the sign or see the sign, just put on your hat and come on."

"So long," the man say, "and don't step on the corn hills whilst a-goin'."

This old man was mighty old by then. He got to feelin' more and more poorly. His eyes got dimmer and his ears got weaker, and in two-three months he couldn't neither see nor hear a thing. He was deaf and he was blind.

One mornin' a letter come. It was a sign from Death. But the old man couldn't read it, 'cause he's blind. Four-five days later Death sent a man to give him the sign to hear. The man say, "Death sent me to give you the sign to hear." But the old man couldn't hear a word, and he didn't put on his hat and go.

So Death came himself. He looked and saw the old man was deaf and blind and couldn't neither see a sign nor hear it. He was mad. "You fooled me, Old Man," he say. "I'm not comin' back no more."

The old man got more poorly all the time, but he didn't die, 'cause Death had passed him by. His beard got longer and scragglier all the time, and he wasted away till there wasn't hardly nothin' to him. He kept tendin' his corn, but he couldn't see where he was goin' and got to fallin' and tanglin' up with the stalks. He got so thin and poorly one day he just altogether disappear.

But if you look on the corn ears you can see that there's some hair hangin' on the ends. That's some of the wicked old man's whiskers he lost whilst fallin' around 'mongst the cornstalks.

Folks say he never died, just disappeared.

THE MOON'S
A WOMAN

> River's all muddy,
> Creek's gone dry,
> If it wasn't for the woman
> The men'd all die.

WELL, what you reckon the answer to that is? Just look at it this way. The sun's a man and the moon's a woman. The sun is regular 'bout his habits, always in the same place at the same time, isn't he? But the moon's changeable, now, isn't she? It's the changing of the moon that gives us rain. If it didn't ever rain three hundred sixty-five days a year, the sun would set the world on fire, wouldn't it? And if the moon didn't ever change, then it wouldn't ever rain, would it, and there wouldn't be no water in the creeks *or* rivers, would there? And that bein' the case, everything would dry up and the men'd all die, wouldn't they? That's what I'm sayin'.

> River's all muddy,
> Creek's gone dry,
> If it wasn't for the woman
> The men'd all die.

The moon's a woman and the sun's a man. That's what I'm talkin' about.

Now, back to the 'tato patch and clean out the pigweed. Don't break it off, either, pull it out by the roots.

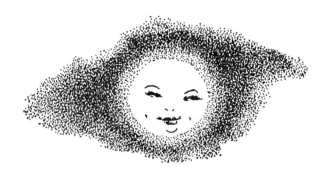

NOTES ON THE STORIES

Anyone who explores the field of U.S. Negro folklore must be impressed with its richness and variety. We find animal tales of diverse kinds, anecdotes or incidents which through the passing years have been elevated to the category of legend, apocryphal stories of the old plantation master and the plantation boss who came later, accounts of the Devil's endless attempts to corrupt people, stories about field hands, yarns of the supernatural, and narratives based on Old Testament themes. There are riddles, tall tales or "lies," and fragments of old proverbs that emerge from their hiding places under the most casual and unexpected circumstances. In addition, a considerable amount of story material is found in secular songs. The group worksong has long been a vehicle for the presentation of dramatic, almost legendary tales, such as "Long John," "John Henry," "Grizzly Bear" and others of a similar kind. A vast documentation of Negro folklore in the United States exists, and some of the stories in this small collection are probably well known in one variant or another. Others are less well known, and among them are a few, at least, which may be in print for the first time.

All except one of the tales in this book were gathered in rural areas of Alabama, New Jersey and Michigan from Negro narrators. Alabama storytellers who contributed were Rich Amerson of Halsel, Celina Lewis of Livingston, Hubert Townsend of East York, a preacher of Bogue Chitta whose name I do not recall, Red Willie

Smith who originally came from the Georgia coast area, Dock Stevens
from near Silacauga, James Prestwood from near Selma, and others.
A few of the stories were told to me in Michigan by people who had
come originally from southern states, among them Arthur Edwards
and Samuel Harper. Two of the tales were heard in a migratory farm
camp a few miles out of Englishtown, New Jersey.

One of the first problems that arises in transcribing American Negro
stories concerns the use of dialect. It has always been my general belief
that a story that is completely dependent on dialect for its success is
essentially not a very good one. And one may argue with validity that
if Negro speech *requires* dialect treatment, so too does much of the
White speech of the South—or, for that matter, the speech of Brook-
lyn, the Midwest or the Southwest. Yet it must be recognized that
the American Negro has developed special cultural patterns, and it
is difficult to think of Negro lore dissociated from the people and the
setting which produced it. The rhythm of the Negro storyteller's
speech and his use of language are as vital as the direction, pacing,
settings and lighting of a drama in the theater. In transcribing these
tales I have tried to be faithful in spirit to the originals, at the same
time avoiding "dialect" where it is merely "quaint" or "amusing." But
wherever the speech of the narrator seemed to me to contribute to
the imagery and movement of a tale, I have tried to preserve it.

No two people tell a story in precisely the same way. There are
regional differences in speech, and there are personal differences in
the use of imagery and dramatic effects. To some extent I have tried
to eliminate some of the more conspicuous differences, and to bring
all the tales into a least common denominator, stylistically speaking,
as though they had been told originally by the same person.

While we tend to think of human tales and animal tales as belonging to different categories, choice of characters is sometimes a matter
of local tradition or personal preference. In some tales, for example,
the protagonists are John and Old Boss; but the same stories are
known in different variants with animal characters. SHARING THE
CROPS, in this collection, is known elsewhere with animal actors.
And BUH RABBIT's HUMAN WEAKNESS, told here with a cast of
animal actors, has other versions in which human preachers are fea-
tured. While the Brer Rabbit stories do form a cycle, the possibility
of interchange of characters suggests that the moral point or the
incident is the most important element.

Many Negro stories which at first glance seem like pointless adventures may nevertheless have a social comment to make. One such implicit point runs through the whole Buh Rabbit cycle—that size and strength do not necessarily spell victory over the physically weak. BUH MOUSE TESTIFIES is a commentary on human behavior. THE SKULL and BUH RABBIT'S HUMAN WEAKNESS emphasize the importance of knowing when to keep your own confidence. DEVIL IN CHURCH notes that if you don't want to be conspicuous you mustn't behave like an outsider.

Tales that explain the beginning of things are not overly common in U.S. Negro folklore. Frequently the explanation of a particular phenomenon seems almost incidental to the story itself, as in BUH RABBIT'S TAIL. TERRAPIN'S POT OF SENSE explains why living creatures have their sense in their heads; this revelation is understated, though the narrator stresses that the terrapin's fall from the tree accounts for the cracked appearance of the creature's back.

A rather large number of U.S. Negro tales have West African precedents, though the settings and characters may have been altered, and the central point been changed or forgotten. The tar man story, for example, is a simple case of trapping the mischief-making rabbit (either for stealing garden produce or water from a well), who then outwits his captor by clever talk. Among the Ashanti in West Africa the tar man is the instrument for capturing the spider trickster, Anansi, who is stealing from his own family during a famine. The Anansi version is laden with moral implications, and concludes with an explanation of why spiders are found hiding in dark corners. (See "Anansi Plays Dead" in Courlander, *The Hat-Shaking Dance*, Harcourt Brace and Co., 1956.)

Some Anansi stories are still told in the South. In various communities along the Georgia coast the term "Anansi tales" is used to indicate stories not told in polite company. Elsewhere Anansi fills the role which by and large has been taken over by Buh Rabbit. In Louisiana, which had a sustained cultural contact with the West Indies, it is possible to hear stories in which the trickster and his victim are known as Malice and Bouqui, a human comedy team familiar in Haiti, Guadaloupe, Martinique and other Creole-speaking islands. While Buh Rabbit has an unmistakable New World character, his relationship to the spider trickster and the hare trickster of West Africa is clear. He is also a distant cousin of the hare trickster of Southeast Asia, and of the mouse deer of Indonesia and Malaya; some of the escapades of these Eastern tricksters are duplicated in Buh Rabbit's repertoire.

WAITING ON SALVATION: A tale that is heard in many forms over a wide area of the South. Some related variants explain why the buzzard migrated from the North to the South; he waits for his fresh meat to season up and smell bad, and comes back to find that someone has buried it, so he migrates to a place where they "never bury the dead." (See Richard M. Dorson, *Negro Folktales in Michigan*, Harvard University Press, 1956.) In one version heard in Alabama, Buh Wolf starts talking about fresh meat, and the buzzard's stomach is upset at the thought. "Man," he says, "be still, can't you? Don't you see me eatin'?"

REFORM MEETING: This story comes from an old Livingston, Alabama, newspaper, and was discovered by Ruby Pickens Tartt. There are numerous such tales built around community meetings to discuss problems. (See for example BUH MOUSE TESTIFIES.) In this story we see a specific application of the proverb "Reform begins at home."

RABBIT, FOX, AND THE RAIL FENCE: One of Buh Rabbit's picaresque adventures with Buh Fox. It recalls an Indonesian story in which the mouse deer escapes from his captor by getting him to put his nose in a split bamboo tree, where it is pinched fast.

BUH RABBIT'S TIGHT NECKTIE: A version of a widely-told tale in the Buh Rabbit series. Although no moral point is suggested, the theme is subtly related to the widely dispersed story of the animal befriended who turns against his benefactor. Countless variants of this plot are known in Asia, Europe and Africa. In Indonesia, the buffalo saves the crocodile from certain death, whereupon the crocodile attempts to eat him; in Ethiopia a man saves a snake pursued by hunters, and the snake then threatens to eat him; in India, a man aids a tiger, with the same result. In all of these more elaborate tales the intended victim is saved by a ruse on the part of a third party, often the local trickster hero. In this United States variant the element of Buh Rabbit's actually aiding the snake is missing, and thus there is no moral issue involved. Buh Rabbit is depicted not as taking the snake to warm him up, but as using him for his own purposes.

TERRAPIN'S POT OF SENSE: This story is clearly related to the West African Ashanti tale which explains why wisdom is found everywhere. In the Ashanti version, Anansi, the spider trickster, is trying to corner all the wisdom in the world. He gathers it, places it in an earthen pot, and tries to carry it up into a high tree. But he carries the pot in front of him and finds it difficult to climb. His son Intikuma comes on the scene and advises him to carry the pot on his back. In embarrassment and rage that he has had to receive advice from a little boy, even though he carries a potful of wisdom, Anansi hurls the pot to the ground and shatters it. All the other animals come and retrieve bits of wisdom and carry it away. The moral point of the tale is that "One head can't go into consultation." (See "Why Wisdom Is Found Everywhere," in *The Hat-Shaking Dance*, ibid.)

SLOW TRAIN TO ARKANSAS: A tale that is known in many forms in different parts of the world, with various animals participating in the race. Always, however, the race goes not to the swiftest of creatures but to the smartest. Numerous variants of the plot are known in the United States. In one such version the race is between Buh Deer and Buh Snail. Buh Snail holds on to the deer's tail, and when Buh Deer arrives at his destination Buh Snail drops off and says, "Here I am, Buh Deer, what kept you so long?"

BUH RABBIT'S HUMAN WEAKNESS: Here we have a tale with a humorous twist and a well-phrased moral point at the end. In some variants the characters are human preachers rather than animal.

BUH RABBIT'S BIG EAT: This is a tale meant for the natural-born story-teller, devoid of moral point, except that Rabbit revenges himself against Alligator. A good portion of the entertainment value lies in projecting the excitement of all the animals doing their tricks, while Alligator unknowingly waits for disaster. The story is also told with Buh Bear the victim. (See "The Bear Meets Trouble" in *Negro Folk-tales in Michigan*, ibid.)

BUH FOX'S NUMBER NINE SHOES: As this tale is told elsewhere, on the Georgia coast, shoes aren't required for the deception of Buh Bear. Rabbit lies down on the road and pretends to be dead. Buh Bear (or Buh Wolf) comes along with his cart of fish. He pauses to look at the rabbit and says: "Now if I only had *two* like that I could have a mighty fine rabbit stew." He drives on, while Buh Rabbit gets up, runs through the field and lies down again in the road ahead of the cart. When Buh Bear sees him for the second time he stops and says:

"Now I got a brace of rabbits." He throws Buh Rabbit in the cart with the fish and walks back to get the first one. When he is out of sight, Buh Rabbit drives off with the fish. In a Gulla version of the story, recorded by Guy B. Johnson, the dupe is a man. When Buh Wolf tries the same trick on the man, it is too late.

Buh Rabbit's Tail: The denouement of this story, explaining why Rabbit has a short tail, is very much like an episode in Mexican lore in which the trickster hero, Señor Coyote, similarly harangues his various organs and limbs, finally exiling his tail from his place of safety. In this way, he is seized by the waiting dogs. (See Dan Storm, *Picture Tales from Mexico*, Lippincott, 1941.)

The Well: Many U.S. variants of this story include the tar man episode. When the rabbit persists in using the well which he refused to help dig, the animals make the tar man to capture him. There is a Haitian tale which tells how the frog was made chief of the well. He refuses to let the animals drink, and his downfall comes when God arrives to see what the matter is. Frog is so infatuated with his position as guardian that he tells God to go away. Both the United States and Haitian versions seem related to a West African tale in which the Sky God appoints Frog custodian of his well during a drouth. One by one Frog turns the thirsting animals away, and acts in the same manner when the Sky God arrives. In anger, the Sky God takes away the frog's tail. (See "Nyame's Well" in *The Hat-Shaking Dance*, ibid.)

Rabbit Scratches Buh Elephant's Back: A U.S. Negro version of a tale found in Indonesia, Malaya, Burma and elsewhere in Asia and Africa. In the Indonesian story it is the mouse deer who plays the trickster role. The elephant has lost a bet to the tiger, and the tiger is scheduled to eat him. The mouse deer gets on the elephant's back, pretends to be killing him, and frightens the tiger away. (See "The Bet Between Matjan and Gadja" in Courlander, *Kantchil's Lime Pit*, Harcourt Brace and Co., 1950.)

Buh Mouse Testifies: A commentary on one of the sad facts of life, that the sins of the strong are sometimes overlooked and go unpunished, while the weak sometimes suffer innocently. It recalls an Ethiopian tale in which the donkey is punished by the stronger, meat-eating animals for nibbling grass. (See "The Donkey Who Sinned" in Courlander and Leslau, *The Fire On the Mountain*, Holt, 1950.)

BUH RABBIT'S GRAVEYARD: Here is a theme found in trickster tales in many cultures—the frightening off of a strong adversary by means of threatening talk. It recalls how Buh Rabbit frightens off the wolf in the story BUH RABBIT SCRATCHES BUH ELEPHANT'S BACK. The denouement of the tale concerning the sharing of the crops reminds one of the Haitian story telling how Bouqui and Ti Malice divide their fishing spoils. Variants are found elsewhere in the United States, the West Indies and West Africa.

BUH RABBIT AND THE KING: Here we have an American version of a tale familiar in West Africa. In the West African version Anansi, the spider trickster, captures hornets instead of blackbirds. He captures the large snake by the same method under the pretense of measuring his length. The Ashanti form of the story explains how Anansi came to own all tales. When he delivers the python, the hornets and the leopard to Nyame, the Sky God (who becomes the King in the U.S. version), Nyame gives him all the stories in the world. This tale was heard in Alabama, but is well known in eastern Georgia, particularly in the Sea Islands. It has also been preserved in Jamaica and other islands of the West Indies.

THE TEXAS SANDSTORM: A tale of gross exaggeration, reminiscent of a good many of the frontier yarns in the Pecos Bill and Davy Crockett tradition.

HOT TIMES: Another "big lie" story. It seems to belong to a variety of Negro tall tales in which the listener isn't expected to believe a word of what is said. Similar exaggerations are applied to such themes as mosquitoes, rain and fog.

THE CHAMPION: This story has the quality of an actual incident, but it is known in several forms, with various ruses for frightening off the adversary. One version recorded in Michigan (Dorson, ibid.) has the slave slap the master's wife, the logic being that a slave who'd do that wouldn't be afraid of anything. All of the variants with which I am familiar have a slavery setting. One old man in Bogue Chitta, Alabama, declared that the matching of plantation champions was a widespread "sport" in slavery times.

THE SKULL: The story of the talking skull has many counterparts in far-flung parts of the world. Tales with the skull as the object on which the plot turns are told throughout West Africa. (See "The Young Man and the Skull" in Heli Chatelain, *Folk Tales of Angola,* American Folklore Society, 1894.) Another version accounting for the origin of the coconut is known in Burma. (See "The Origin of the Cocoanut" in Maung Htin Aung, *Burmese Folk-Tales,* Oxford University Press, 1948.) It tells of a mischief-maker who was beheaded by the king. An officer finds the head talking the next day and reports the matter to the king, who promptly investigates. When the head refuses to speak, the officer too is beheaded, whereupon the first head speaks. The king orders the mischief-maker's head buried deeply so that it will cause no more trouble, and it grows into a coconut tree. And if you shake a coconut and place it against your ear you will hear a gurgling inside—the mischief-maker still gossiping. Related to this theme is the West African tale of the singing tortoise which refuses to sing when the community is told about his ability. (See "The Singing Tortoise" in Courlander and Herzog, *The Cow-tail Switch,* Holt, 1947.) Variants with the singing tortoise as the miraculous object are known in Haiti and southern United States.

OLD MASTER AND OKRA: Old Master, the slave owner of pre-Civil War days, figures in numerous Negro folk tales. Often he is found in the company of a slave named John or George. Characteristic of some of the Old Master stories is the seemingly intimate relationship between the slave and his owner. The slave is often portrayed as somewhat on the silly side, but with an undercurrent of sly wit with which he survives trying experiences. There is at least indirect evidence that some form of this story was known in slavery days. Lincoln is reported to have cited a similar incident at a cabinet meeting when, after a long silence, his cabinet began to pour out criticism of a plan he had offered. Lincoln then told the anecdote about a slave who greeted his returning master with the words: "Master, Master! The off-ox (left-hand ox) run away. The other one run away too. I didn't tell you both together, I wanted to break it easy."

THE DO-ALL AX: This appears to be an ancient tale, most immediately related to West African variants. Among the Ashanti of Gold Coast the magic instrument is a hoe belonging to the porcupine. The hoe is stolen by Anansi, the spider, who doesn't know the word to stop it, and it hoes itself away and is never seen again. (See Rattray, *Akan-Ashanti Folk-Tales,* Oxford, 1931.) There is another Ashanti story with the Sorcerer's Apprentice theme in which the magic instrument is a sword, also stolen by Anansi. Anansi fails to stop the sword after sending it against the enemy; having slaughtered all the enemy, it turns against Anansi's army and finally Anansi himself. (See "The Sword That Fought by Itself" in *The Hat-Shaking Dance,* ibid.) The general theme of not being able to stop a magical device is of course widely known in European lore. In southern United States the magic hoe is a familiar folk theme, often detached from the story setting. But a complete story version exists, as well. A magic hoe tale found on Wilmington Island, Georgia, is almost identical with the Ashanti story, with Buh Rabbit and Buh Wolf replacing the spider and the porcupine. (See *Drums and Shadows,* compiled by the Georgia Writers' Project, University of Georgia Press, 1940.) Flying slaves, also mentioned in the opening of THE DO-ALL AX, are commonly mentioned in U.S. Negro folklore. The name of the chief character of the story, Kwako, is of special interest; not only is it of West African origin, but it appears to be a fragmentary recollection of Anansi the spider, often called Kwaku Anansi, or "Uncle" Anansi.

THE KING AND KUFFIE: A story of apparent Yoruba origin. A variant is known in Cuba, with Yoruba deities playing the roles here taken by the King and Kuffie. (See "The Beef Tongue of Orula" in Courlander, *Ride With the Sun,* McGraw-Hill, 1955.) The name Kuffie, in some parts of southern United States pronounced Coffee, comes from the West African (Ashanti) Kofi, a name given to a boy born on Thursday.

OLD BOSS, JOHN, AND THE MULE: This is reminiscent of THE SKULL in respect to the talking object or animal that doesn't speak when witnesses arrive. A somewhat similar situation is found in one West African story. Inanimate objects begin to talk and frighten people, who run in panic to the chief. He sends them all away in disgust, whereupon his stool comments: "Fantastic, isn't it? Imagine, a talking yam!" (See "Talk" in *The Cow-tail Switch*, ibid. Other United States variants are found under the title "TheTalking Mule," in Dorson, ibid., and in Zora Neale Hurston's *Mules and Men*, Lippincott, 1935.)

CROSSING THE RIVER: While in this story it happens to be the field hand John who misinterprets the bullfrog's croaking, as told by other narrators the victim is variously the Preacher or the Irishman. There are numerous similar stories about the Irishman, who as an immigrant was an object of good-humored amusement in Negro tales.

OLD BOSS AND GEORGE: An anecdote about a field hand in which everything depends on the sophisticated punch line. This yarn is also known in rural Michigan.

DEVIL IN CHURCH: This tale was told by a preacher near Bogue Chitta, Alabama, to illustrate a point. While I was on a music recording field trip in this region in 1950 I asked permission to record the Sunday service of the Shiloh Primitive Baptist Church. At church time the building was crowded, and not one but four neighborhood preachers were present. One of the preachers looked around and laughed, saying, "Sure is a big gathering today. When folks see other folks doing something, they got to get in there and do it too. It's like the Devil in church." After the service I asked him about the Devil in church. This is the story he told.

PREACHER AND THE DEVIL: This incident is strikingly similar (in reverse) to a story told in Lebanon, in which a priest delivers a sermon on St. George and the Dragon. Prompted by a member of the congregation who thinks the priest's exaggerations are too gross to swallow, the priest progressively shortens the length of the dragon's tail until at last it disappears altogether. (See Habib T. Katibah, *Arabian Romances and Folk Tales*, Scribners, 1929.) In the U.S. Negro version, the measuring of the dead Goliath's body as stretching from "Shochoh to Jerusalem" reminds one of the Somali story in which Moses slays the giant Ojje Ben Onogh, whose corpse stretches from Burao to Berbera. (See "Ojje Ben Onogh" in *The Fire on the Mountain*, ibid.)

WHAT THE PREACHER'S TALKING ABOUT: A Turkish version of this story is found in Ramsay and McCullagh, *Tales from Turkey*, Simpson, Marshall, Hamilton, Kent and Co., 1914.

SHARING THE CROPS: Another rendition of this tale employs Buh Bear and Buh Rabbit, instead of humans, as characters. (See "Brazos Bottom Philosophy" by A. W. Eddins in *Southwestern Lore*, No. 9, 1931.) It is likely that even where animal protagonists are used, the imagery that is evoked is that of the poor Negro sharecropper and the relatively well-to-do, probably white, landowner. It may well be that, as in West Africa, the animal tale is often a disguised story about humans. When Buh Bear and Buh Rabbit play the roles of the landowner and the sharecropper, the story assumes the quality of a metaphor—talking about one thing in terms of another.

DEATH AND THE OLD MAN: This is a local form of a widespread folktale, most commonly encountered in Europe, in which a man bargains with Death, who is forced to pass him by. A variant known in Russia has the man trap Death in a bag, with the consequence that nobody dies and there is much suffering among the sick and aged. Because of his trick, the man responsible is never called for by Death, and life becomes an unbearable burden to him. In a related U.S. Negro tale, a wicked man outwits the Devil who comes for him. When the man dies he is not permitted to enter heaven, and the Devil, who fears him, will not permit him to enter hell either. The Devil hands him a hot coal and tells him to go off and start a hell of his own somewhere else.

THE MOON'S A WOMAN: This appears to be an old riddle, with the sun represented as a male and the moon as a female who replenishes the water of the rivers. As presented here it is in more simplified form than the original. In its normal setting, where riddles of this type were told, the narrator probably would pause after the rhyme and wait for someone to give the answer. Here the storyteller handles both question and answer as though it were taken for granted that no one else present knows the answer.